AQUARIUM LIFE

354 FULL COLOR ILLUSTRATIONS

AQUARIUM LIFE

by Vanna Dal Vesco   Wolfgang Klausewitz   Bruno Peyronel   Enrico Tortonese

Photographs by Giuseppe Mazza

CHARTWELL BOOKS INC.

110 ENTERPRISE AVE.
SECAUCUS, N. J. 07094

ISBN 1-55521-292-1
Published by Chartwell Books Inc., a division of Book Sales Inc.,
110 Enterprise Avenue, Secaucus, N. J. 07094

Originally published in Italian by
Arnoldo Mondadori Editore, Milan
© 1974 Arnoldo Mondadori Editore
English translation © 1975 Octopus Books Limited

Illustrations and captions for this book were prepared by
Redazione Opere Enciclopediche for the publisher
Arnoldo Mondadori.
The drawings were prepared by Giambattista Bertelli,
Piero Cozzaglio, Raffaele Curiel and Gastone Rossini.

Acknowledgments

The publisher would like to thank the companies
Nuku-Nuku, Moana Club and Ornis of Milan for the
specimens which were supplied for photography. The
publisher also thanks Acquario Civico of Milan for the
specimens on pages 60 left, 87 top right and 92, and
Acquario Tropicale of Syracuse for the specimens on
pages 85 bottom right and 87 bottom right.

Printed in Spain by Artes Graficas Toledo,S.A.
D.L.TO:720-1988

Contents

Introduction

Aquaria are becoming more and more popular in modern society which, in principle, is an excellent thing, since it gives us an opportunity to observe living things, learn their way of life and reflect on their needs, thus making us more aware of our natural environment. However, should a newly acquired aquarium become an additional decoration to our living-room, and the creatures in it only be looked upon as means of entertainment — rather like actors on a stage — not only would its educative value be lost, but all our effort and expense would have been wasted, because we will soon find out that we could not keep the aquarium going for long if we did not learn to respect the life in it. In this book the aquarium has been described as a whole ecological unit, and rightly so, because, within it, the fish and their environment are closely connected and their relationships and inter-acting can neither be ignored nor separated. The first step towards setting up an aquarium should be to gain sufficient knowledge of the vegetation and conditions of the environment favourable to the particular fishes envisaged as inhabitants, not forgetting to take into account the likes and dislikes of each individual species, so that peaceful co-existence can be obtained, and success can follow.

In this respect it is my pleasure to introduce this book. It is authoritative and beautifully presented and, throughout, careful consideration and emphasis has been given to the two most fundamental and related problems of aquaria: good technical knowledge and skill when setting up or maintaining a tank, coupled with love and care in choosing the contents which should be looked upon as a living world, where behavioural patterns and relationships — either sympathetic or antagonistic — of the different species have been fully taken into account. Each section of the book has been written by eminent specialists — botanists Bruno Peyronel and Vanna Dal Vesco (for plants), zoologist Enrico Tortonese (animals), naturalist and aquarist Wolfgang Klausewitz (practical advice for the aquarist). They have excelled themselves in treating the subject in its entirety and in a style simple enough to make this a book which will appeal to a wide range of readers.

The combination of superb artistry and high standards displayed by the photographer, Giuseppe Mazza, cannot pass unmentioned in the introduction of a book such as this, where words alone could never have done full justice to the beauty and colourful splendour of each species of underwater plants and animals, from the modest muddy pond, to the depths of the tropical oceans, with their brilliant display of coral reefs and exotic inhabitants. Some of the photographs reproduced in this book are of specimens that can only be kept in large public aquaria and, by including them in his work, Giuseppe Mazza has matched the skill of the writers. Many readers will find that the beautiful illustrations of so many fascinating creatures will act as a revelation and stimulus for them to go and visit an aquarium where they can learn more and see the specimens in the flesh.

Some of the qualities of this book are obvious; others can only be appreciated by reading it and learning how much life can be enriched by taking a keen interest in living creatures, by setting up a tank and keeping an aquarium as an object of interest and pleasure and not just as an ornament to the home. The book has great merit and more than deserves my good wishes for its continued success. By reading the text and looking at the superb colour photographs the readers of this book will be made aware that, unlike other hobbies pursued as an end in itself and for popularity alone, keeping an aquarium can be a great source of intellectual enrichment and pleasure.

Sandro Ruffo
Director of the Civic Museum
of Natural History, Verona

Plants

THE ROLE OF PLANTS IN AN AQUARIUM

Often an aquarium is looked upon only as something made to contain living fish. This a wrong concept for various reasons. It is important to realize that setting up a tank and keeping fish can, and should, give pleasure and satisfaction far beyond that of looking at some fish living in a glass-cage.

An aquarium is, in fact, an ecosystem in its own right where different kinds of plants and animals live in harmony with each other, and as far as possible in conditions similar to their natural environment. The aquatic world has its own laws of equilibrium, and we must try to learn and to adopt these laws in the planning and setting up of an aquarium, if we want to achieve success. Given the right approach and a little knowledge, an aquarium can be made into a miniature ecosystem which is almost completely self-sufficient and needing little support from outside. There are, of course, some fundamental points to take into account when planning an aquarium. For instance some fish species are predators on smaller fishes and cannot be kept in mixed communities; a constant balance must be kept between production and consumption of both oxygen and food; a means of dispos-ing of waste matter must be devised by the introduction of some appro-priate organisms, and so on.

The spherical fish-bowl containing just a few goldfish is the smallest and least ambitious form of aquarium, but this is hardly a self-maintaining ecosystem. Life in it is entirely dependent on man's intervention for maintenance and survival. Because it lacks plant life the vital processes of oxygen production and absorption of carbon dioxide cannot take place, no smaller animals can survive; its limited surface area restricts the number and type of fish that can be kept. In fact a balanced ecosystem is impossible to establish under these conditions.

Clearly, then, keeping a fish-bowl would soon turn into a monotonous routine of tasks for the amateur and, one assumes, is not likely to make a happy home for the fish or one in which they would live long, because they are thus being forced to live in a completely artificial environment. However, we can learn from this simple form of fish-keeping a funda-mental principle that guides all forms of life: this is that the survival of any given species requires the right bal-ance between it and its surroundings. The isolation of individuals is detri-mental to their welfare. The basic truth has been proved in specialized

Opposite page: A thick clump of a tropical aquarium plant. Beside their ornamental value, plants have a very useful function in aquaria, because they are nourished by the animals' waste matter, they produce oxygen, reduce the level of carbon dioxide, and serve as food to herbivorous animals.

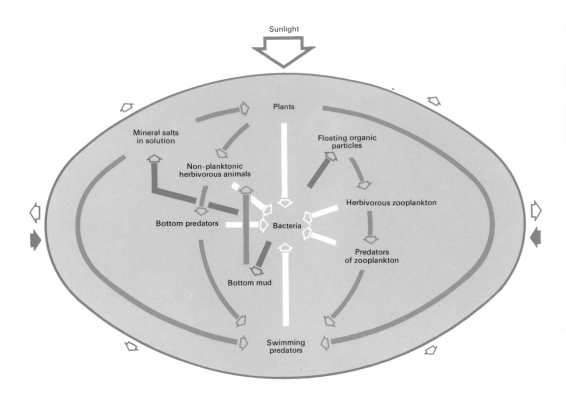

Sunlight

Plants

Mineral salts
in solution

Non-planktonic
herbivorous animals

Floating organic
particles

Bottom predators

Bacteria

Herbivorous zooplankton

Predators
of zooplankton

Bottom mud

Swimming
predators

Diagram showing the food web in lakes or ponds. Blue arrows indicate the flow of food substances; white arrows indicate the process of decomposition, due to bacterial activity on mineral and dead organic matter; green arrows show the result of bacterial activity. The green arrows outside the diagram show mineral salts carried in solution by the river water to a lake; the white arrows indicate mineral salts flowing back to the river, and both together show the loss of animal and plant life suffered by the lake due to predatory terrestrial animals or other factors.

farming, too, where man has to make continuous efforts and is dependent on all sorts of artificial substitutes in the form of fertilizers, weed-killers, insecticides etc. in order to grow any specialized single crop away from its own native conditions.

It is best, therefore, to try to aim for an ecological unit which is as large and complex as possible, so that it can give the maximum satisfaction and pleasure as a hobby and has the advantage of greater self-support and easier care in order to retain its balance. This is where aquatic plants have an important role to play.

First of all plants have a productive role. The green plant is, in fact, the only living thing capable of transforming non-organic matter (minerals contained in the soil or dissolved in water) into organic substances (such as carbohydrates, fats and proteins), and only requiring sunlight for this process. As an added bonus, in the course of this transformation, plants absorb carbon dioxide and release oxygen.

In an ideally planned aquarium, plants fulfil more than one important need. They purify the water by reducing the level of carbon dioxide and utilizing waste matter for their own nourishment. They provide oxygen for animal respiration and serve as food for herbivorous organisms; which, in turn serve

as a source of food for carnivorous species. Ideal conditions can never be achieved in full, of course, and a certain amount of careful intervention is still required on the part of the aquarist. This, however can be reduced to a minimum, while the satisfaction and pleasure given by creating an environment congenial to fish and pleasing to look at more than compensates both for the expenditure and effort initially put into it. On the whole, nature can look after itself, and man's interference with it will be due not to necessity, but more to his wish to heighten the qualities of his life. Caring for aquaria teaches us discretion, because as soon as we lose our sympathy with the balance of nature we are faced with disaster. Only recently have we come to realize how mistakenly modern society has tried to dominate and shape the whole world into a technological wonder designed for man's convenience at the expense of nature, and in so doing, we have created a number of problems which will never be solved unless we regain some of our almost forgotten natural ways.

Apart from purifying the water and providing food for animals, aquatic plants can make an ideal place of refuge for a shy fish or give a suitable location for laying eggs. Other fishes

10

choose pieces of vegetation as building material for their nests.

Lastly we must remember how valuable plants are, aesthetically speaking. Surely a tank without vegetation would be as uninteresting to behold as a garden without flowers. Aquarium plants often look most elegant in their inherent forms and colours and we would even go as far as to say that a tank containing only plants is more acceptable than one containing only fish. After all, it is quite common to keep plants in pots around the house and they look well enough, while the sight of fish swimming dejectedly in water alone has the same sadness as that of birds kept in a bare cage, lacking even the comfort of a small perch.

We cannot close this subject without dealing at this stage and once and for all with something which is far too often a common sight in aquaria: that is artificial plants. They obviously cannot perform any of the many useful functions of true vegetation. Aesthetically they are in bad taste and if, in spite of this, we make room for them, then we should logically accept plastic fish as well. Surely this inanimate imitation of life could only be considered an absurd monstrosity by our readers and should thus be studiously avoided for the reasons set out above.

THE PHYSICAL CHARACTERISTICS AND LIFE-CYCLE OF AQUATIC PLANTS

Water plants are simply ordinary plants that have the specialized ability to grow partly or wholly under water. Because of the limitation of space we can only give a summary description of the physical characteristics and growth of water plants and begin with a few generalities about plant-life.

The higher plants are anchored to the ground normally by roots through which food is absorbed and transmitted to the green parts (foliage) which are particularly adapted to transform and assimilate the food. The third main part of a plant is of course its means of reproduction (usually in the form of flowers).

The roots of a plant differ in size and shape according to the nature and condition of the soil, as well as in specific differences. Roots absorb water containing nourishing substances, such as salts and other elements necessary to plant life. These elements are many, but the most important from the point of view of quantity besides hydrogen and oxygen, the components of water, are nitrogen, potassium, calcium, phosphorous and sulphur; however, trace elements such as iron, copper, borax, manganese must be present,

A lake: a natural ecosystem. There is a balance of actions and reactions within it that keeps all its life in equilibrium.

11

An aquarium is a reconstruction of a natural self-supporting environment, in which there is a perfectly balanced exchange of vital substances. If this balance can be achieved, there should be no need for any intervention by the aquarist, such as providing food or changing the water.

Nymphoides aquatica, a plant only suitable for tropical aquaria. It grows equally well either floating or submerged.
For propagation it needs putting in shallow water with plenty of light: it will then grow lateral shoots, which can be separated to form new plants.

Diagram illustrating photosynthesis taking place on the leaves of *Bacopa amplexicaulis.* With the aid of sunlight (energy), plants transform non-organic matter (mineral salts, etc.) into organic substances (sugars, fats, proteins, etc.). In the course of this process, plants release oxygen and absorb carbon dioxide. Photosynthesis occurs mainly on the foliage and all the green parts of a plant.

Synnema triflorum, an aquatic plant originating from India and the Malayan peninsula. A very elegant species, suited for tropical aquariums.

even though only in microscopic proportion.

A chemical process of vital importance, called photosynthesis, takes place thoughout the foliage and other green parts of the plant. The green plant is able to use the sunlight to combine the carbon dioxide (taken from the air) with the water and salt brought in through the roots, and transforms this mixture into organic substances. First we have sugar and starch, and then vegetable fats and proteins. Photosynthesis is a process of tremendous importance because it is the only means that nature has to transform the elements present in air, water and earth into organic food. Without this first step, the plant would be unable to support, firstly herbivorous animals and, indirectly carnivorous animals and man.

The process of photosynthesis can be formulated as follows:

$$CO_2 \quad\quad H_2O$$
carbon dioxide + water +
$$C_6H_{12}O_6 \quad\quad O_2$$
energy → sugar + oxygen

Solar energy is essential to combine the simple substances such as water, carbon dioxide and various salts, into a more complicated compound, sugars (as in the example given above), vegetable fats, and proteins. In the course of this chemical reaction another important point is to be noted; that is the release of oxygen. This is certainly an important factor, as 90% of all oxygen contained in the earth's atmosphere is produced by plants during the process of photosynthesis. Green plants perform a further air purification role by absorbing carbon dioxide, which, although not poisonous, is not suitable for animal respiration.

Water, too, has more than one role to play: it participates directly in the chemical process of photosynthesis and carries other substances and at the same time distributes food by carrying the organic substances obtained to other parts of the plant, once the process is completed. Generally speaking a large quantity of water must be taken in before the plant absorbs the right amount of salts, as these are usually in the form of weak solutions. Plants eliminate the excess water by a process akin to perspiration which occurs through the minute pores or stomata covering the surface of the leaves and which act as water regulators.

In all living plants (as well as animals) there takes place a process, *respiration*, which can be roughly approximated to the opposite of photosynthesis and is represented as follows, overleaf:

15

$C_6H_{12}O_6$ O_2 H_2O
  sugar + oxygen → water +
CO_2
  carbon dioxide + energy

Energy is now released and used by the plant for its growth, movement, heat, light and so on. The process of photosynthesis can only take place in the presence of sunlight, and it is far superior in intensity than breathing; for this reason the respiration of the plant can only be measured in the dark in the absence of photosynthesis, when the carbon dioxide released by the plant is added to that produced by the other organisms living in the same environment. Photosynthesis, however, remains the more important activity in plants even when they are exposed to exactly equal periods of sunlight and darkness.

Reproduction of higher plants is usually achieved through its flowers. Pollen is the fertilizing agent and seeds are formed usually within a fruit, after the flower has been pollinated. There are, however, plants that can reproduce themselves in other ways. Some by releasing spores (single-cell organisms) capable of self-reproduction; some by shoots; some by the ability to grow new roots when a branch is in contact with the soil, some by cuttings and so on.

Water plants have different ways and degrees of adaptation to aquatic life. Many are completely submerged, only reaching the surface with their flowers (for example, Tape-grass, *Vallisneria*); some have only their lower half submerged (Arrow-head, *Sagittaria*); and some have fixed roots and floating leaves and flowers (Water lilies, *Nymphaeaceae*) and, yet again, some are completely and freely floating in water (Duck-weed, *Lemma*). There are also some specialized plants that grow in ponds and are adapted so as to live in mud under humid atmospheric conditions, but these are not usually of much interest to aquarists. Environment has a direct bearing on the specialized characteristics of aquatic plants. We all know that water differs from air, but the difference is not readily apparent to all.

First of all water is denser than air and contains far less oxygen than the atmosphere. On the other hand, the salts and mineral substances, so vital to plant life, can be dissolved and carried much more easily in water than in air. The most obvious advantage of all is that plants are not likely to run out of water while living in it.

From these facts, it is easy to guess the nature of the variations we can expect in water plants. They must obviously have some adaptation to overcome the lower oxygen content

of water, while they can dispense with the water retention mechanisms which are vital to plants growing in the open air to avoid dehydration. Therefore it follows that the surface tissues of aquatic plants (thus not needing to play a role of mechanical protection against external elements and water loss, as is the case in their exposed counterparts) are always very thin and adapted to speed up the exchange between the plants and their environment, such as the passage of oxygen, carbon dioxide and various mineral solutions. All the submerged parts of aquatic plants are usually much reduced in size and submerged leaves or segments are often filiform. This factor increases the total area of contact between the plant and the water, giving not only a more efficient means of exchange to the plant, but also acting as a water-break against the violence of currents or strong waves. In plants that have partly submerged foliage one can observe how the submerged leaves have adapted to aquatic conditions, causing the phenomenon of two different forms of leaves on the same plant. When floating, leaves are equpped with their own miniature air-filled floats, which can be found either around the edges or above the stalks and are made up of special spongy tissues.

Whenever aquatic plants have stomata (water retention regulating pores, placed on the lower part of ordinary leaves) they only appear on the upperside of floating leaves and disappear when the leaves are submerged.

The roots, too, are somewhat reduced. Floating plants do not need anchoring and plants that live under water can absorb sufficient food through their leaves and stems. In some cases the roots disappear completely.

When plants are only partly under water, they often have some special aerating fibres forming channels through which air passes into the submerged part from the upper part of the plant.

Variations also occur to adapt the aquatic plant to reproduction under special conditions, such as transport of pollen, dispersion of seeds and spores through current.

CULTIVATION OF AQUATIC PLANTS

Once again, with the limitation of space, we can only mention essential points, leaving the details for reference to other specialized works.

Water. Water can be of two types: hard water when it is rich in limestone and other minerals, and soft water when the mineral content is very low. Usually tropical waters are extremely

17

This plant has underwater (submerged) leaves of a totally different shape to those above the surface, a phenomenon common amongst the higher plants growing in water. Submerged leaves are thinner to increase the surface area in contact with the water, so as to facilitate gaseous exchange between the plant and its environment.

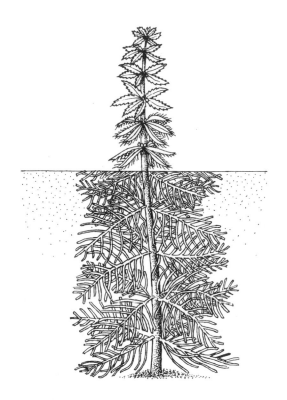

soft, often completely free of salts. European waters vary considerably, but are generally hard and at times even very hard. Therefore special care should be taken when growing tropical plants as some tap water can be too hard on them and may need softening either by filtering or by the addition of distilled water.

The chemical condition of the water is also important. This is measured technically by assessing the hydrogen ions in the water so that pH 7 represents neutral. A pH below this indicates acidity; a higher value represents alkalinity. Normally it is found that our water has a low acidity and this can be corrected by adding some matter, such as chalk, which within a matter of days brings the value pH to around 6·5. However one must obviously cater individually according to the selection of the fish and then add the appropriate vegetation.

Soil and fertilizers. Contrary to what many aquarists believe, sand on its own is not always a suitable base for aquarium plants. Coarse sand can only be used on its own when many animals are kept in poor light and there is enough waste matter built up and decomposed to provide nourishment for the plants. In all other cases some other type of suitably selected and bacteria-free soil must be added —

some turf mixed with the sand is useful for increasing aeration.

The main types of soils are:

Sand — river sand is preferable if possible. It must always be well washed and left to season as much as possible in the open air. It should not contain iron or soluble lime.

Silt or loam should be well dried and seasoned indoors for at least 6 months before being sieved and used in a very fine form.

Leaf mould — the best type is from ash leaves. It should be well seasoned and kept dry in the open air and should only be used with coarse sand.

Peat is best bought already prepared from a gardening shop and it is used mixed with sand.

Field-earth is easily gathered from mole-hills. Some loam should be added to it before use.

Compost is not safe in aquaria unless it has been well seasoned for at least two years. It is always used mixed with sand and often with peat too.

We shall give advice for the choice of soil suitable to the particular plants, as we go along. Obviously one has to choose either the right kinds of plants for a given soil or the soil to suit the plants, because of the large variation in requirements between aquatic species. There is however a compromise which enables one to over-

come this limitation. Plants can first be individually planted in separate glass bowls, containing the right mixture of soil for each plant and then placed strategically under the bottom layer in the tank. This will help to produce a greater variety and is also useful when either the plants or the bottom soil have to be changed.

If a good number of fishes and a rich soil are put in the aquarium at the beginning one will find that it will take quite a while before it becomes necessary to add fertilizers. Naturally this is not the case when a few fishes are kept in a tank with plain sand on the bottom. It is always important to check that the substances added as fertilizers are absolutely safe for the fish. Some fertilizing pills which can be buried under the soil are quite good. In soft water with a low lime content we may notice a low level of carbon dioxide. A good cure for this is the addition of about 200 cc of soda water daily, evenly distributed through the tank, and ideally first thing in the morning.

Light and temperature. Position and lighting have a direct bearing on the growth of plants in an aquarium. The amount and degree of light required by the different species of aquatic plants varies a great deal. Some need bright sunlight throughout the day (water-lilies), some only a good light but more or less limited to the morning or evening (submerged plants such as *Cabomba* or water buttercups) and yet others only need shady illumination (as in the case of the *Cryptocoryne*). The table of light requirements (page 23) gives the amount needed by the most common plants used in aquaria. It can be seen from this that sunlight is beneficial to the majority because of its importance in photosynthesis. The most efficient direction is light from above and, as the intensity of sunlight diminishes in direct proportion to the distance from a window, the most favourable position is by either a south-east or a south-west window. However the location is often restricted in a home by space etc. A north light can still be suitable especially in the summer. The use of artificial light is necessary normally during the winter months and when an aquarium is not near a window. Diffused light from fluorescent tubes is better than conventional electric bulbs for this purpose, and some attention should be given to the intensity of both light and heat released by the tube. The most suitable are the 3 kW tubes. The amount of heat required by a plant (as with the light) depends on the particular species and its original geographical

Left: *Cardamine lyrata*, a plant native to eastern China, Korea and Japan. Suitable for both tropical and cold aquaria.
Right: *Nomaphila stricta*, from Thailand, the Malayan peninsula and Indonesia. It loves hard water and reproduces by underground shoots.

19

Flowers and leaves of *Nymphaea alba*. Water-lilies are the most eye-catching of floating species. They are too large to be grown in small indoor aquariums, but they are widely used in open-air ponds and hot-house aquaria.

environment. Tropical plants usually need a range between 23° and 27°C, temperate zone specimens between 11° and 19°C. Excess heat (above 40°C) is ultimately lethal to all plants, but very low temperatures will not kill plants, only arrest their growth for the time being. Even amongst tropical species plants exist, some *Cryptocoryne* for example, which require very little heat, and do quite well at 20°C. Even species of the genus *Hygrophila* still grow when the temperature goes as low as 12°C. There are some species in the temperate zone which are also common in subtropical waters; it is wise to find out their place of origin in order to establish their particular heat requirement. Generally it is found that a temporary drop of temperature does no harm apart from slowing down their growth, but any attempt to try and acclimatize them to cooler conditions has been so far fruitless.

Propagation. Many water plants are self-producing and often so much so that they need to be thinned out, but others need some more elaborate means of propagation. In general seeds are seldom used in aquaria; the more common method is by cuttings which grow easily enough, once in contact with the soil. It is better to put the cuttings down in little bunches

to have a more attractive result. Under the right conditions many plants reproduce themselves by growing runners or lateral buds or shoots which grow into additional plants. Once these latter are well developed and strong they can easily be detached and re-planted.

Hibernation. Some problems may arise from the habit of some species of hibernating. Originally, due to the seasonal changes in conditions occurring in their original environment, a fixed rhythm of growth and rest was established. Seasonal changes in the temperate zone and droughts in tropical conditions are responsible for this annual cycle, as well as the variations of sunlight hours through the year. Submerged plants are easily dealt with, as their growth is constant; it is more difficult to cope with floating varieties, which must sometimes be kept under peat or other damp fibres in a humid and warm atmosphere. To avoid too many complications, it is wise to check this point before choosing the plant.

PLANT CARE

Insufficient light. This causes shrinkage of leaves (especially around the edges) and elongation of the stems, so that the plants become 'leggy'; the loss of chlorophyll follows

20

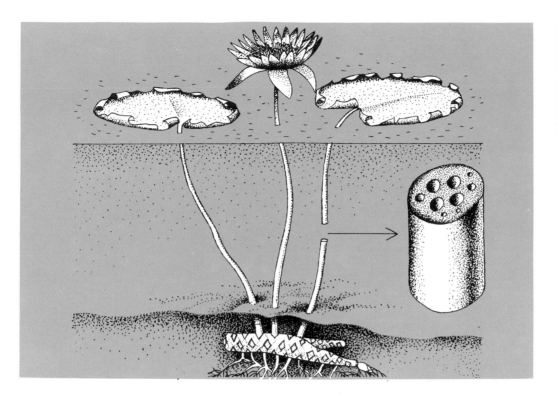

Horizontal section of a water-lily stalk. Partly submerged plants have air channels that allow the flow of air from the exposed parts to the underwater tissues, so that they too have an efficient exchange of gases.

and the green parts fade, turn yellowish, and begin to look unhealthy. The provision of a richer soil will not cure this problem. In fact, it could make it worse as the organic matter decomposes, using up oxygen until the water is poisonous to life. The only answer is to arrange far better lighting.

Poor nourishment. As already mentioned in connection with the soil, it is sometimes necessary to add some fertilizer. Often the trouble is due to the absence of *trace elements*, while all other substances including nitrogen, potassium, phosphorus are well balanced. The absence of iron, in particular, can cause *chlorosis* (yellowish, fading green leaves) as iron is necessary to the production of chlorophyll. The disease can be cured by the supply of 30 drops of 10% sulphate of iron solution diluted in 10 litres of water, given weekly. However it would be better to prevent the trouble by a complete change of the impoverished soil with a fresh, rich, new mixture every two years.

Mutual antipathy. This word indicates the influence that organisms can exert on each other. In the case of some plants, reciprocal allergy can develop and growth stops when two species are close to each other, while they return to normal again, as soon as they are separated. These is a lot to

learn about these phenomena occurring in aquaria, but we know, for example, that *Echinodorus* and *Cryptocoryne* are compatible, while the same *Cryptocoryne* can reduce the growth of *Sagittaria* and *Vallisneria* when placed next to them.

Frost, scorching from the sun, desiccation from a dry atmosphere. There is little likelihood of any of these problems arising in indoor aquaria. However the leaves of floating, or partly submerged, plants can be scorched when the tank is exposed to too much sunlight and some damage can be done from a too dry atmosphere when there is no lid.

Algae and bacteria. Algae can cause great damage to underwater growth. Some single-celled algae, which give a green colouring to the water and the walls of the tank, are relatively harmless. The blue algae (*Cyanophicae*), however, can do a lot of damage. Their presence is indicative of bad water conditions or other growing faults, such as poor light or organic decomposition of the soil. The algicides are of little help in this case, and the best thing would be a complete new start; i.e. changing water, soil and plants. Filamentous algae are less harmful by nature, but if they become dominant (which can happen when the tank is in strong light) can threaten

21

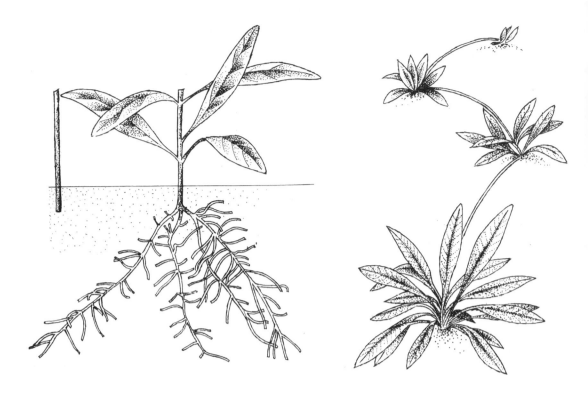

the movement and even the freedom of small fish and other delicate organisms, that can be trapped, or even choked, by the mass of filaments. If this happens, once again the answer is a complete change of the contents. The growth of harmless brown seaweeds is always a sign of poor light.

Animal pests. In this field the main offender is the water snail, which eats underwater plants particularly broad-leaved plants; they can be detected by the roundish holes which they eat out of the leaves. Not all snails cause damage, because some do not attack plants at all, some only feed on specific plants, and others only eat plants if no other food is available to them. Even a few fish eat plants: for example the mollies and a number of species of characin and cyprinid. Aphids that at times attack vegetation exposed to the air are rather difficult to eliminate, as most insecticides capable of destroying them are also fatal to fish. Floating plants can best be removed to another container for disinfestation and later washed clean of insecticide before replacing them in the tank.

LOCATION OF PLANTS IN AQUARIA

First decide upon the choice of plants (not forgetting to check on points of reciprocal compatibility as well as their suitability to the animal life), and then set about acquiring them. Possibly some could be obtained from the surrounding countryside but in view of the likelihood of introducing pests and diseases this is not recommended. Others can only be bought from specialized shops. It is essential to give all plants a period of *quarantine* by putting them in a container at first rather than in the tank intended as their final permanent home. This precaution is necessary to avoid the introduction of diseases and pests in the tank.

We have already talked about suitable kinds of soils but it is important to remember to try to obtain a sloping surface of the bottom layer, by building up the back and gradually coming down at the front edge of the aquarium. A thin covering of gravel or pebbles will prevent the water becoming clouded when disturbed, will help keep the plants on the bottom, and will prevent the peat from floating to the top. The plants must be arranged so that those needing the most sunlight will be placed on the outer side of a tank kept directly by a window, always taking size into account, so that the larger ones are put at the back and do not shade or hide the smaller ones which are best at the front of the tank. The best effect is probably obtained by

Left: diagram of vegetative reproduction of a plant. A small section of the stalk is planted and, after a short while, it grows roots and starts a new growth.
Right: spontaneous reproduction by runners.

22

Very Bright Light	Bright Light	Moderate Light
Azolla caroliniana	*Aponogeton distachyus*	*Aponogeton* (except *A. distachyus*)
Cabomba	*Ceratopteris*	*Cryptocoryne*
Callitriche	*Echinodorus ranunculoides*	*Echinodorus* (except *E. ranunculoides* & *grandiflorus*)
Ceratophyllum	*Fontinalis*	*Heleocharis prolifera*
Echinodorus grandiflorus	*Helocharis acicularis*	*Isoëtes lacustris*
Eichornia	*Elodes densa*	*Nitella*
Elodea callitrichoides	*Heteranthera*	
Elodea canadensis	*Hippuris*	
Marsilia hirsuta	*Lagarosiphon*	
Nymphaea	*Lemna*	
Pistia	*Ludwigia*	
Pontederia	*Marsilia quadrifolia*	
Potamogeton	*Myriophyllum*	
Sagittaria montevidensis	*Riccia*	
Sagittaria sagittifolia	*Salvinia*	
	Utricularie exoleta	

limiting the number of plants according to the volume of the tank, arranging them in little scattered clumps strategically placed with the larger broad leaved varieties at the back, still visible through the spaces left by daintier groups gradually staggered towards the front. However, remember to leave enough room for the fish to move freely around them, and thin out excessive growth when necessary. Do not overlook one last important point, and that is never to let more than one third of the surface of the water be covered by floating vegetation.

MARINE AQUARIA
Attempts to keep marine plants in aquaria have not, so far, given good results. Almost all sea plants, from the primitive seaweeds to the marine flowering plants (such as *Zostera* — eel grass, and *Posidonia*) seem to die as soon as they are removed from the sea, and leave a trail of harmful decomposition when placed in the aquarium. At the most, if one lives by the sea, one can introduce a few pebbles covered with algae (*Corallina*, *Lithothamnion*) which seem to be safe, provided they are changed fairly frequently.

CRYPTOGAMS (ALGAE, LIVERWORTS, AND MOSSES)
Chara. A genus of green algae growing submerged in fresh or salt water rich in lime salts. Their rather delicate long stalks bear verticils that become whitish because of incrustations of lime salt. In general, they resemble the *Ceratophyllum* but they are rather fragile and not very decorative. Some species, for example, *Chara foetida*, *C. hispida*, *C. fragilis* and *C. vulgaris*, need little light and could grow in tanks kept away from direct light, filled with cold or slightly warm water, but they are not recommended for cultivation as a rule.

Nitella flexilis. A species of green algae similar to those of the genus *Chara* in appearance as well as characteristics. It grows in fresh and salt waters within the northern temperate zone. It has upright fronds each branching into two, and is more or less green in colour and completely submerged. Aquarists favour it greatly because fish like to lay their eggs on it. It is easy to grow, in that it withstands relatively high temperatures, and grows throughout the winter, needing little light. It is easily propagated from cuttings dropped into the water. For best results, however, it should be firmly planted by fixing its small roots into the mud.

Riccia. A genus of liverwort (bryophyte) widely found floating on stagnant or slow-moving waters through-

The table gives an approximate guide to the light requirements of a few species most commonly grown in aquaria.
Left: list of plants requiring very bright light; centre, those needing bright light; right, those requiring moderately bright light.

23

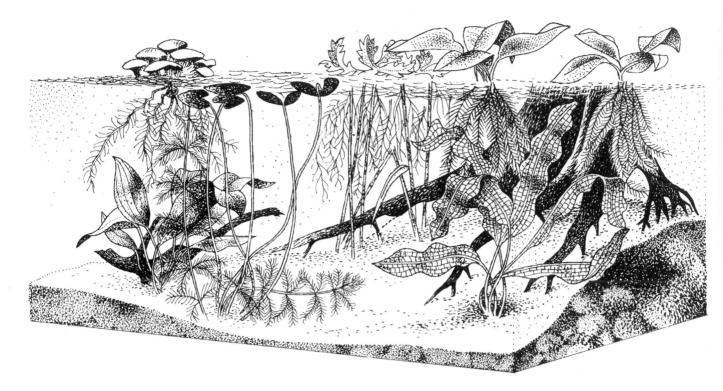

out the world, and also able to survive in mud. The best known species is *Riccia fluitans*, a plant with a fleshy thallus, about 1 mm across, which branches dichotomously (into pairs) and which is bright green in colour. This fleshy growth can form masses of varying sizes, filled with microfauna, where fishes can lay their eggs and be provided with shelter for their newly hatched young. This rather decorative plant thrives both in cold and warm water and, given artificial illumination, grows in the winter too. It prefers soft water rich in organic matter.

Ricciocarpus natans. This, too, is a liverwort, fairly well represented in almost all parts of the world. It is found either floating on ponds, small lakes and puddles, or, out of water, growing in the muddy waterside banks. Its fleshy body is larger than *Riccia*, reaching a length of 2 cm and with its extremity heart-shaped, thick and cut by longitudinal grooves. Its root-like growths (rhizoids) are immersed in the water. *Ricciocarpus natans* requires more light than members of the genus *Riccia* and even in ideal conditions its growth is slow. It is sensitive to temperatures higher than 22 °C and likes fairly soft water. It does not grow well when near other plants. In the aquarium it serves the same uses as *Riccia*.

Fontinalis. A genus of moss (bryophyte) living under water in small rivers in Europe, northern Asia and North America. The leaves are always of lanceolate formation, often carinate, rather small and ranging from an olive to a vivid green colour. The fronds, often fairly long, are rooted on the bottom preferably on stones.

These plants like good but indirect sunlight; fresh clear water (rain water is ideal) frequently replaced and low temperatures in order to retain their green foliage. If the water is too hot, they wilt and will become covered in algae. Therefore they make a more suitable decoration for cold-water aquaria, where they provide fishes with an excellent place to lay their eggs. The best type of soil is a mixture of peat and sand with an upper layer of small stones which help to hold them in little groups of branchlets. It is possible to gather stones covered with *Fontinalis* directly from local streams, but it is often found that the changes of conditions of the water affect the plant adversely and it is not recommended.

Amongst the most commonly grown species are: *Fontinalis antipyretica* with small olive green leaves placed in clusters of three; *Fontinalis gracilis*, which is even smaller; and *Fontinalis squamosa* with a thick growth of

fronds and very dark green foliage.

Amblystegium. A genus of moss of small to medium size, found in all climatic zones. They have straight fronds in the shape of low cushions with small lanceolate leaves. They are similar to the *Fontinalis* species in their need for soft water, but much easier to grow as they withstand a greater range of temperatures. Provided they have a suitable type of water, they quickly develop an underwater growth so thick that it will need periodical thinning out.

Isoëtes. A genus of fern (family Isoetaceae) growing from rhizomes with leaves more or less ribbon-shaped, light green and straight. They require a mainly sandy soil mixed with some peat and mould. They love light but not direct sunlight. They are not easy to grow, and not very attractive in looks. The better known species are: *Isoetes echinospora, I. lacustris* (the Quillwort), *I. malinverniana*.

Ceratopteris. A genus of the fern family Parkeriaceae common to the hot regions on the whole world (many are Asiatic and some American) either floating or fixed on the muddy bottom. They have leaves ending in a star-shaped rosette and are of two types. Those which float at the surface or just underwater do not bear spores, are more or less twisted and have markings which differ from those on the fertile leaves. The spore-bearing leaves have very narrow segments and stand erect in the water. The sterile leaves have supplementary growths along their edges which can detach themselves and become additional plants.

The species of the genus *Ceratopteris* require tepid to warm water (24° to 30°C) slightly acid and free of limestone: the sand should be very coarse and mixed with lots of silt and a little peat, and the light should be well diffused. Given these conditions, the plants will do well and can either be left free in the water or fixed to the bottom with small pebbles. These very attractive plants are also useful in giving shelter to other organisms, but their tender leaves are often damaged or eaten by fish and molluscs. The species most commonly kept in aquaria are *Ceratopteris thalictroides* and *C. pteridioides*. An underwater variety of the first, with finely fringed leaves, is called 'Sumatra fern' and is one of the most popular species, due to its elegant form.

Marsilia. A genus of fern (family Marsiliaceae) which lives in the northern temperate zone, growing in stagnant fresh water. Its members have thin rhizoids anchored at the bottom, with long filamentous stems, each

supporting a cluster of four ovate leaves with smooth edges, reminiscent of clover.

They need cold to tepid water and soil mixed with peat, but they are not very suitable for small indoor aquaria due to the plain appearance of their submerged stems and the fact that their leaves can often get very untidy. The best known species are: *Marsilia quadrifolia,* which commonly grows in rice fields, and the Australian *M. hirsuta.*

Salvinia. A genus of ferns (family Salvinaceae) and are floating plants common to Europe, Asia, and America. They have two small oval-shaped, green leaves which are smooth and floating, while a third is transformed into a feathery branch similar to little roots hanging below the water. They are very pretty plants, good for water decoration, but have no other use. The best known species is *Salvinia natans,* but *S. auriculata* is more widely kept in aquaria. It comes from tropical America and has roundish leaves. It needs lots of light and warmth (about 20° to 22°C but easily stands a maximum of 30°C), fairly soft water, and a damp atmosphere, which can be created by covering the tank with a lid. It must be regularly trimmed to avoid its spreading all over the available water surface.

Azolla caroliniana. A dainty fern of the family Azollaceae originating from the southern part of the United States and isolated areas of Central and South America, but now established in many parts of Europe. It has small, divergent, ovate leaves, either green or reddish in colour, forming small flat-leaved clumps which float on the surface. It is suitable for tanks kept at a temperature range of 16° to 26°C with a good diffused light coming from above. The water must be very soft (it is best to add rainwater). It grows rapidly and needs regular trimming. A similar species is *A. filiculoides,* which has deeply lobed leaves or fronds.

DICOTYLEDONOUS HIGHER PLANTS

Nymphaea. The water-lilies of the family Nymphaeaceae of tropical and temperate zones of the whole world, having roundish or oval-shaped leaves floating at the water's surface and bearing long stems reaching down to the bottom mud where they are attached to rhizoid roots. Often the flowers are very large and consist of four greenish sepals and many fleshy petals that can be white or coloured. They often, too, have a delicate scent and always float at the surface. They are the most famous water-lilies, the most eye-catching of all water surface plants, widely reared in their many

species, varieties and hybrids, in tanks and bowls, in the open or in hot-house nurseries.

In temperate to warm water (18° to 28°C) in larger tanks with chalky-sand bottom soil, some good results can be obtained in the cultivation of smaller varieties, provided young plants are used. We suggest *Nymphaea baumii*, a variety from Angola, with round floating leaves and white flowers 2 to 3 cm across. It needs water of not less than 30 to 40 cm in depth. *N. stellata* is another suitable small type, with submerged leaves which are smaller than the floating leaves with serrated edges; it bears small, light blue flowers.

Cabomba. A genus of the family Nymphaeaceae. This is the most beautiful group of water plants and much coveted by aquarists. The most commonly grown species are: *Cabomba aquatica* from tropical America, which bears leaves placed at the same height on opposite sides, each with a roundish outline and divided into five finely segmented lobes. These leaves are submerged (very seldom floating leaves are formed, and then only at flowering time); and *C. furcata* from central Brazil, shorter than the latter and with coarser leaves. Both species thrive in a temperature ranging between 18° to 30°C. From the southern parts of North America comes *C.*

caroliniana, with foliage similar to that of *C. aquatica*, but slightly larger and less finely subdivided. Some of the varieties have reddish leaves (for example *C. mulertii*). This species is also easier to grow than *C. aquatica*, but they are not plants for beginners, who would do best to start with *Limnophila heterophylla* and *L. sessiliflora* which look very similar.

To obtain good results in rearing the species of *Cabomba* three conditions must be fulfilled: (i) very good illumination but no direct sunlight, for instance, the best place for the tank is by an east-facing window where there is only a short period of morning sunlight; (ii) absolutely soft water with a slight acid base (pH about 6·5 filtering on peat); (ii) soil made up from coarse sand mixed with a little sandy leaf mould, peat and seasoned silt. Cabombas spread by means of shoots from the roots.

Ceratophyllum demersum. Species of the family Ceratophyllaceae common in fresh water all over temperate and tropical zones. It has finely divided foliage, the leaves growing in pairs well spaced up the stems, which may be 2 metres long. They have insignificant looking flowers. Very similar to it is *Ceratophyllum submersum* from Europe and tropical zones of Asia, with a much thinner growth—

and with more finely divided leaves. Ceratophyllum species are quite decorative and suitable for a well lighted aquarium with fresh clear water. The naturally free floating plants can be fixed with small pebbles at the bottom of the tank, and given some time, they will grow into small bushy clumps. Fish find them useful places to lay the eggs. If the plant becomes overgrown it is best to cut the upper part part and replant it, and eliminate the lower part. Should they get covered in dirt they can be lifted and rinsed under a tap and then replaced in the tank.

Ranunculus. A genus of the family Ranunculaceae which includes a few aquatic species (belonging to the *Ranunculus aquatilis* group); they look attractive, but are not really suitable for the aquarium as they have a short life, are very demanding on light requirements and are prone to collect harmful algae.

Subularia aquatica. A species of the family Cruciferae which ranges in size from 2 to 8 cm, has long grass-like leaves and lives in the northern hemisphere. It is a long lasting, undemanding plant that benefits from light coming from above. It grows pretty little white flowers which float at the water surface in summer. It is rarely grown, but deserves more consideration.

Aldrovanda vesiculosa. A species of the family Droseraceae widespread in still waters all over Europe and Southern Asia. It is a submerged insect-eating plant and its main characteristic is the adaptation of its leaves into tiny bladders capable of catching minute aquatic animals. It can be an interesting curiosity in its own right, but it would be unwise to put it in a tank where fish are bred, as it could catch the newly hatched fish.

Callitriche. A genus of the family Euphorbiaceae, widely distributed, that can grow submerged or floating on water with rather delicate branched stems and tiny leaves (less than half a centimetre) mainly elongate, sometimes ovate in shape when floating, and insignificant flowers.

Very suitable for cold aquaria and grows well throughout all seasons. They require no special soil (they even grow in sand alone); prefer soft water and good illumination. They are easily propagated from shoots, especially if cut between nodules. The most popular species are: *Callitriche stagnalis*, the 'water starworts' common in Europe and Asia; *C. hermaphroditica* from Europe and North America is the most popular in aquaria; *C. palustris* is indigenous to Europe and North America. All these species are very similar to each other.

Left: *Ceratophyllum demersum*.
Right: A species of *Cabomba*.

29

A species of *Callitriche*, suitable for cold aquaria.

Ludwigia palustris. Family Anagraceae. A species which lives in ponds completely or partly submerged, in temperate regions of northern Europe. The leaves are placed opposite one another on the stem, and usually ovate, but can vary in shape being also pointed or blunt. They have long trailing stems that root easily at the nodes and rather dull flowers. This plant will grow in water of cold to moderate temperature, needs a rich soil and illumination from above. It is easily reared, but perhaps less suitable for growing completely submerged than the American species. These last are in the greatest demand as aquarium specimens because they thrive when grown submerged and they withstand higher temperatures. They too need strong light and prefer a soil mixture of forest mould and silt.

The North American *Ludwigia alternifolia* is worth mentioning in connection with the American species. It is similar in appearance to *L. palustris* but has more pointed leaves of beautiful formation which have shades of red or purple on the lower part (for example *L. mulertii*). It also withstands moderately hot water. *L. natans* is a native of the southern regions of North America and is similar to the last species described, apart from its having rather smaller leaves and long

roots growing out from the nodes.

Myriophyllum. Family Aloragaceae. This genus includes some forty species, four of which are indigenous to Europe. The rest are exotic and often grown in aquaria. Apart from a single exception they are all completely submerged with finely divided leaves and upright stems. Whole smooth-edged floating leaves may be developed at the surface and these bear the fairly plain flowers.

The European species of *Myriophyllum*, commonly known as 'milfoils' are suitable for well lit aquaria with cold water. They require little attention (apart from normal care) and will grow in sand mixed with some loam. In these conditions they retain their green foliage throughout the year and make a particularly attractive ornamental plant for the tank. It is advisable to clean the plants now and again to free them from the dirt trapped between the fine foliage.

The different species are all very similar and this makes identification rather difficult. A few European species can be mentioned: *Myriophyllum alternifolium*, the leaves of which are borne on upright stems and are finely pinnate with 3 to 4 lobes, dark green in colour; *M. verticillatum*, with thin pointed leaves; *M. spicatum*, indigenous to Europe and southern Asia,

Flowers of *Ranunculus aquatilis*: a plant with a rather short aquarium life.

A species of *Ludwigia*, a very popular aquatic species for cold aquaria.

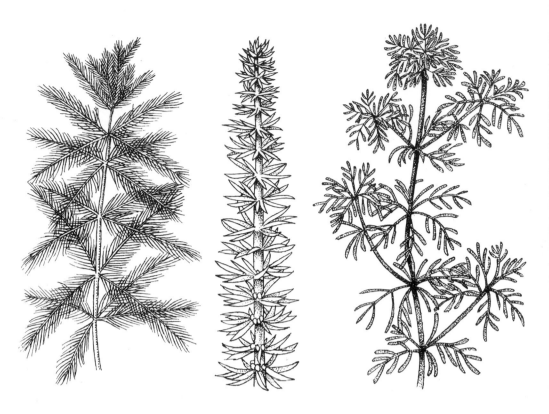

and *M. heterophyllum*, from Europe and the southern part of the United States, which has alternate leaves, which are thicker than in other species. As in the case of the *Ludwigia*, the American species are more favoured than are the European species for cultivation. They differ in having a better growth rate, are better looking and last longer. They have the same requirements as our native species, but withstand higher temperatures of up to 20°C. All species, including the European ones are used by egg-laying fishes.

Amongst the exotic species are: *Myriophyllum proserpinacoides* (=*M. brasiliense*), ranging over the southern part of Brazil and throughout Argentina; with submerged pinnate leaves divided into five lobes of a characteristic grey-green colour, and with buds that grow above the water bearing shorter, but stronger leaves. It requires little attention and grows on plain sand, but needs a good light and a damp atmosphere for the welfare of the part above water (tanks with lid sprays are ideal). It does well in temperatures ranging between 15° and 24°C. *M. pinnatum*, from the southern United States to Panama often has alternate leaves, which are thick and hair-like.

M. hippuroides of North America,

particularly in the Atlantic States has fine and long pinnate leaves up to 4 cm in length, arranged on upright stems. *M. prismatum*, a species probably originating from North America, is similar to the one described above, apart from having thinner and longer leaves of a lighter colour. *M. eggelingii* has fine and very dark green leaves.

Prosperpinaca palustris. Family Aloragaceae – North and Central American species, very similar to *Myriophyllum* and equally suitable as an aquarium specimen. It needs plenty of light; withstands higher temperatures and grows best in harder water.

Hippuris vulgaris. Family Hippuridaceae – species found in Europe, northern Asia and scattered through North and South America, commonly called 'marestail'. It grows in erect clumps with long flat leaves which grow from the stem in whorls. The leaves are shorter when they grow above water. It is suitable for cold aquaria with hard water (a few fragments of limestone can be added), it needs good light but not direct sunlight (preferably near north-facing window). The soil should be composed of sand and loam, covered with a thin covering of coarse sand, once the stems have been planted. It is a fairly decorative plant, especially if it is grown completely under water.

Left: *Myriophyllum proserpinacoides.*
Centre: *Hippuris vulgaris.*
Right: *Limnophila heterophylla.*

32

Hygrophila polysperma. Family Acantaceae. A species found in the East Indies and in Malaya, with lanceolate rather pointed leaves growing in opposite pairs. The foliage varies in the shade of green being lighter if they are growing above the water surface. This is one of the least demanding water plants and it tolerates temperatures ranging from 10° to 28°C and as high as 30°C; it grows best in a sand and loam mixture, with soft water and good light coming from above stimulates the formation of very large leaves. If it is grown completely under water, it turns into a non-flowering perennial. When growing above the water that part will die late in the autumn.

Hygrophila polysperma is one of the favourites for aquarium culture, mainly because of the dense, light-green foliage which makes a contrast against the darker green or reddish tints of other plants, such as *Cryptocoryne haerteliana*. It spreads by shoots taking root.

Utricularia. Family Lentibulariaceae. An interesting genus of aquatic plants, with long submerged stalks bearing thread-like leaves which divide into pairs. The leaves have little bladders which are capable of trapping small insects. Seasonal, pretty white or yellow flowers grow above the surface of the water. The European species are annual and not suitable for aquaria, where they may be a threat to small fishes. *Utricularia exoleta* from tropical Africa on the other hand, has no roots, its bladders are too small to threaten the survival of newly hatched fish and it can be grown in safety. It does not need much attention and it thrives in tanks in temperate to warm water with good artificial lighting. Its fine foliage is ideal for fish to lay their eggs on.

Limnophila. Family Scrophulariaceae A genus of aquatic plants similar to the *Cabomba* species in appearance. The most handsome is the species *Limnophila gratioloides* (=*Ambulia gratioloides*) from the tropical zones of the Old World, but unfortunately this cannot be recommended for the aquarium, as it contains substances poisonous to fish. Highly recommended are, instead, the *Limnophila heterophylla* and *L. sessiliflora*, both natives of southern Asia, pretty and fairly tough; the leaves are erect, divided into finely lanceolate lobes and grow in clumps completely under water. They do not suffer through poor light and need soft water and soil consisting of sand and loam.

MONOCOTYLEDONOUS HIGHER PLANTS

Aponogeton. Family Aponogeton-

Left: *Myriophyllum spicatum.*
Right: a species of *Hygrophila.*

33

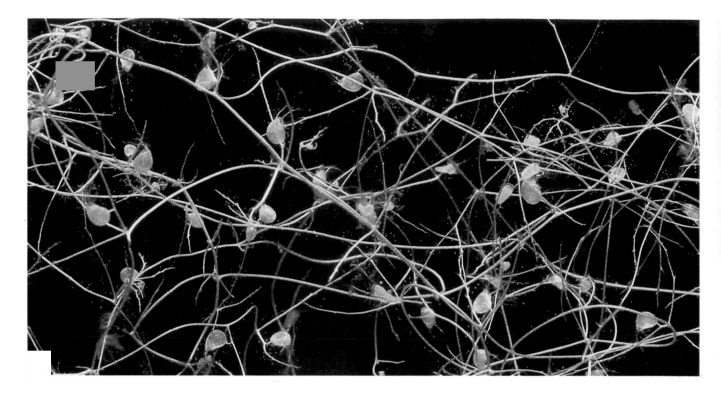

A species of *Utricularia*,
showing the characteristic
small bladder-like growths.

aceae – Africa, southern Asia, northern Australia. The stalks have leaves with smooth edges or only slightly serrated; either lanceolate or strap-like in shape, submerged or floating. In the submerged leaves the tissue often does not form between the veins and as a result they are perforated; these perforations make the process of photosynthesis and the exchange of gases between the plant and the water more efficient. They also reduce the drag of currents. The submerged species loves dim light and needs soft, slightly acid qater (pH 6·5 to 6·0). For best results plant the specimens loosely about 1 cm deep in pots with 3 parts compost, 1 part loam, 2 parts peat and 0·5 g artificial manure. Then place the pots in the bottom layer of the tank. They need relatively warm water, but not much above 25 °C. With good illumination in the tank they grow throughout the year.

Aponogeton fenestralis – Madagascar – The submerged leaves are 20×8 cm long with a smooth edge, rounded, and finely veined, with long stalks. It is a particularly beautiful species, but not recommended for beginners, as it requires skill and a lot of attention. In poor light its foliage attracts algae and dies; it needs diffused lighting, preferably artificially controlled, and likes soft rainwater which must be changed often and corrected for a slight acidity with fragments of peat. It thrives in a soil consisting of coarse sand with a little chalky earth and at temperatures of 14° to 24 °C.

A. ulvaceus – Madagascar – Similar to the above but with longer and narrower leaves which have a wavy outline.

A. dinteri – South West Africa – The primary underwater leaves are elongate, the others have long stalks, are ovate and float on the water, as do the flowers which are yellowish and form a spike measuring about 5 cm in length.

A. distachyus – South Africa – The main leaves are submerged but the others float at the surface, having stalks and elliptic outlines with blunt ends and prominent veins. They grow to a length of up to 20 cm. The flowers are white and grow as a double spike. There are two hybrid forms: var. *grandiflorus* with very large flowers and var. *roseus* with pink flowers. Because oi the long flowering season and the beauty of its blooms, this is one of the most highly recommended of the floating species and is also suitable for outdoor ponds. In the aquarium it is best to pot it separately in soil mixed with loam and peat rather than to plant it in the tank directly. It needs good lighting from

above, direct sun if possible, and a water depth of not less than 30 cm. The temperature must be within a range of 20° to 28°C, but it is advisable to drop it to 5° to 12°C for two months each year (best in the autumn) to give a period of rest to the plant. Some other species are also cultivated, such as *A. crispus* and *A. undulatus*, both submerged and natives of southern Asia and Australia.

Potamogeton. Family Potamogetonaceae. Found in the temperate zone of tropical and subtropical regions in both hemispheres. Their leaves grow submerged or—more rarely—floating on the water, and have varying shapes, mostly alternate with long floating stalks. Its flowers are not outstanding. These plants spread easily by rooting shoots. The European species are good oxygen providers and water purifiers, but are suited to cold aquaria with strong lighting. They need water of medium to low hardness and grow best if some loam is mixed in the soil. It is advisable to use small specimens or plant a runner bearing a bud. The species which have emergent as well as underwater leaves, like *P. natans*, of the temperate and subtropical zones, are not suitable for aquaria, because after some time they grow only floating leaves which contribute nothing

to the aquarium. The submerged species are more successful: *P. lucens* (temperate and subtropical zones); *P. crispus* (temperate zone); *P. perfoliatus* (temperate zone); need cold water and a very strong light from above. In small aquaria the water must be changed weekly. The only difference between the European and exotic species is the longer life the latter seem to have in aquaria and their need for a higher water temperature.

Amongst the numerous other species are *P. compressus* (northern temperate zone); *P. densus* (as before); *P. nodosus* (=*P. fluitans*—temperate and tropical zones); *P. gramineus* (Europe) *P. pusillus* (temperate zone). Some species can be found in our streams and the aquarist can collect them for himself.

Sagittaria. Family Alismataceae — Mainly American species; and *S. sagittifolia* (the Arrow-head) can be found growing wild in Europe. In most cases the wild species have leaves at least partially growing out of water, and more or less arrow-head-shaped. In aquaria, though, they remain completely submerged and are straight, or they produce additional floating ovate leaves. They have flowers with three lobes and three white petals. A few of the species which grow submerged

Left: *Aponogeton ulvaceus*.
Right: Another species of *Aponogeton*.

35

Sagittaria. This genus of
aquatic plants includes
mostly American species.

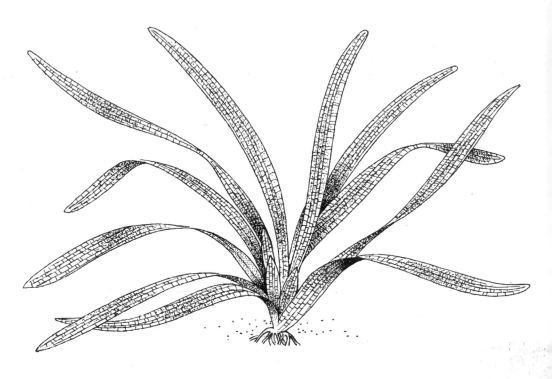

Opposite page: *Potamogeton
densus*.

in aquaria are mentioned below.

Sagittaria subulata — Eastern regions of the United States southwards to Florida. The submerged leaves are similar to those of *Vallisneria*, but more pointed, with the main veins more marked. There is a much smaller variety of this, *pusilla*, with leaves 12 cm long, very pretty and suitable for smaller tanks.

S. platyphylla — From Missouri to Texas It has submerged leaves with multiple veins, long and relatively wide.

All *Sagittaria* species are even less demanding than *Vallisneria*, and thrive in ordinary unwashed sand; growth will increase, and underground shoots will form if some earth or loam are added to the sand. They need good light coming from above; direct sunlight is not essential, but it helps to stimulate flowering. In poorer light growth slows down. Large specimens are best planted in a mixture of earth and loam in glass jars or bowls; this way, one can obtain strong and very beautiful plants, suitable, of course, for aquaria which are big enough. They have no special requirement with regard to water, apart from a slight degree of hardness. In winter the temperature must not fall below 6 °C. They can be grown in heated aquaria too. If kept at 24 °C they do not rest in winter.

Echinodorus. Family Alismataceae — Mainly American with only a few European species. These plants are favoured by aquarists because of the elegant form and the bright green of their leaves, which vary in shape from lanceolate to oblong.

Echinodorus ranunculoides — Europe — It is a marsh plant which can be grown under water, when the leaves become narrower and strictly lanceolate. It is one of the few European species that grow through the winter when kept in an aquarium. It needs good light.

E. radicans — Southern regions of the United States. When cultivated under water this species has wide and semi-transparent oblong leaves vivid green in colour, which makes it a splendid aquarium ornament; unfortunately it does not stand up to submerged culture for very long. It needs sand with a little loam mixed in it, and a slightly dull light if the development of floating leaves is to be avoided, but not too dim otherwise growth slows down; it needs soft water.

E. tenellus, *E. intermedius*, *E. rangeri* — tropical American zones. To this group of species belong the numerous so-called 'Amazon swords', valuable aquarium plants, having narrow long leaves (up to 25 cm). They spread by means of shoots from underground

Hygrophyla polysperma (larger leaves); and *Potamogeton densus.*

runners. If desired, pieces can be cut from the runner and fixed to the bottom for cultivation. They grow well in soft slightly acid water; dim light. The ideal temperatures for these tropical species is around 28°C. They grow particularly well when placed in pots and covered at the bottom of the tank with sand, loam and peat.

E. grandiflorus is also suitable for a well lit large aquarium. It comes from the tropical regions of America and has leaves growing to a length of 30 cm.

Elodea canadensis (=*Anacharis canadensis*) Family Hydrocharitaceae. Native of North America, but widely established in the waters of many European regions, including Italy. This plant, more commonly called 'Elodea' or 'Canadian pondweed' (because of its rapid growth and reproduction) came to Europe at the beginning of the 19th century, probably carried by migratory aquatic birds or by ships. It is a perennial with small ovate leaves, with stems thickly tufted at the top of the stalks; it has small white unisexual flowers. In Europe it produces female plants only, therefore there are no seeds. It grows completely submerged and provides a good supply of oxygen in a tank, but it needs regular thinning, as its fast growth can damage weaker plants

by shading them. It is suited to all kinds of aquaria, provided the water is not too hot; it has no extra requirements and retains its green colour during winter. It tolerates hard water, needs little in the way of nourishing substances, and even thrives without the presence of soil in the water, provided the water is changed weekly. It needs good light from above.

Elodea densa is similar to the species just described, apart from having larger leaves, serrated and more pointed, with a denser more upright growth. It comes from Argentina, as does *H. callitrichoides*, which is more decorative with longer and thinner leaves. Optimum temperature around the 20°C mark.

Lagarosiphon muscoides. Family Hydrocharitaceae—South Africa. This plant is so similar to Elodea that it has often been mistaken for it and known as *Elodea minor* or *E. crispa.* The main difference is in its leaves that curl outwards; it, too, is easy to care for, and its cultivation is as for the *Elodea* species, with better chances of survival in low temperatures.

Vallisneria spiralis. Family Hydrocharitaceae—Tropical and subtropical temperate regions throughout the world. Submerged plants with considerably shortened stalks bearing multi-ribbed leaves, with straight edges

38

Elodea densa: a plant suitable to many types of aquaria.

A species of *Echinodorus*, a much sought after plant for aquaria.

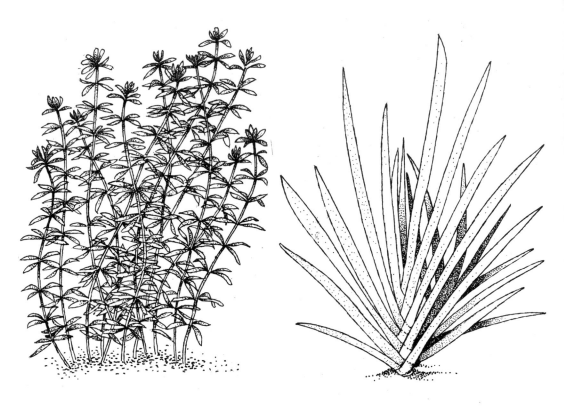

and blunt tips, up to 1 metre long. The female plants form rather insignificant flowers with three carpels to the pistil which reach the surface of the water, being attached to a long thin stem; the male plants produce flowers enclosed by pods and on short stems which release the flowers when mature, and enable them to reach the surface and spread their pollen so that it can reach the female flowers. After pollination the stalks curl downwards and the fruit is ripened under water.

There are some forms of *Vallisneria* with slightly different features: for example, the so-called *V. torta* (*V. spiralis* var. *torta*) and the *V. gigantea* (*V. spiralis* var. *gigantea*) the first with curled leaves; the other with very long and relatively wide leaves. Lastly there are some diminutive varieties particularly suitable for aquaria. All *Vallisneria* species have a constant growth of runners. Their roots are, in most cases, a bluish purple, which helps to differentiate them from the submerged forms of *Sagittaria*.

Vallisneria or Tape-grass is one of the most common and useful of aquarium plants. If a stouter growth is wanted, some fine dry loam can be sprinkled over a mixture of leaf-mould and earth. When planted it is best to cover the shoot only up to the base of the roots; when roots have grown too long,

they must be cut short before replanting. It is advisable to use tanks large enough to leave the *Vallisneria* enough room for free growth. As soon as the roots have taken, the plants will form numerous runners. They need bright light, but they will keep growing, though more slowly, under less favourable conditions. They are generally green and fresh looking at all seasons; a red tinge can occur but it is not characteristic of any given type but seems to be associated with the plant settling down in a new environment. *Vallisneria* are suitable for both heated and cold aquaria; in fact, the temperature can be dropped in winter right down to 4°C without causing any damage. *V. torta* prefers slightly higher temperatures and contrary to widespread belief preserves the crispness of the leaves also in fairly warm water. Some *Vallisneria* species can even be found growing in hot springs at a temperature of 42°C.

Stratiotes aloides. Family Hydrocharitaceae. This submerged plant, commonly known as 'Water Soldier' has large rhizoid roots producing runners and has stiff, lanceolate leaves, with needle-sharp spiny teeth along the margins. The leaves are arranged in a basal tuft with flowers with three green outer sepals and three white petals in an inner row.

40

The stem brings the flower to the surface to bloom. The fruits are fleshy and prickly.

It is a striking and decorative plant, but not suited to aquaria where there ars soft skinned fishes, as these may be wounded when brushing against the saw-like edges of the leaves. In any case an aquarium will require the use of small specimens. It needs strong light and cold water.

Hydrilla verticillata. Family Hydrocharitaceae — southern Asia, Australia, Africa, north-east Europe. The leaves, only up to 2 cm in length, grow in whorls of three to six (as in *Elodea*) with serrated and tassel-like spikes. It has small unassuming looking flowers. It has many varieties and its culture is not difficult as it withstands relatively high temperatures, though it prefers moderately warm water. It grows throughout winter and soil composition is not very important (this plant is mostly floating anyhow); it is an extremely good oxygen producer for the aquarium.

Acorus calamus. Family Araceae — northern temperate zones and southern Asia; **Acorus gramineus** (Japan and China). *Acorus calamus* (the Sweet Flag) and *A. gramineus* are marsh plants, but they have various horticultural and hybrid varieties (white and green, or yellow and green

leaves), which do well when they are kept submerged in tanks. The leaves are long and narrow, but in the var. *pusillus* they only reach 10 cm, and this variety is therefore suitable for small aquaria. They are quite happy in sandy soil, but for stronger growth they can be kept in jars with loamy earth and peat, together with sand. A good precaution is to increase the level of water slowly after positioning the jars in the aquarium and submerge the plants gradually.

Pistia stratiotes. Family Araceae — tropical and partially subtropical zones throughout the world. It is a beautiful floating plant with foliage forming a rosette and leaves of various shapes; generally broad-bladed, rounded, thick, finely fringed, deeply ribbed, and a shade of light grey-green of outstanding beauty. This species has floating thread-like roots; rather dull flowers. It increases by runners. It is one of the most commonly grown and best known of floating plants. It needs plenty of light (possibly direct sunlight), soft and rather warm water. Avoid condensation dripping on it from the lid of the aquarium.

Cryptocoryne. Family Araceae — southern Asia. A genus of plants growing both in marshes and submerged in the shady streams of the Asian tropical forests, but only grown

Left: *Vallisneria spiralis.*
Right: *Cryptocoryne lingua.*

41

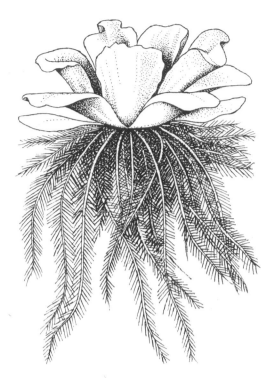

submerged in aquaria. In this case the leaves have stalks, are generally elongated and oval in shape, with curved edges tinted in various shades of green and red. The flower is small and spike-like closely arranged around a soft axis. Hybrid varieties can only be reproduced by cuttings. The following are the main species grown by aquarists: *Cryptocoryne ciliata* (East Indies). The foliage is olive green and brownish red. *C. cordata* (Malayan archipelago), with leaves either grey-green or dark green on top, and reddish-purple underneath. *C. griffithii* (Moluccan peninsular), as above, but with brighter red leaves, very decorative. *C. nevillii* (Ceylon). Light green leaves no longer than 5 cm. *C. willisii* (horticultural form) has even smaller leaves than the last mentioned. Also worthy of mention is *C. pseudo-beckettii* with wavy leaves.

These plants are much appreciated by aquarists as they are very tough and require little attention. Although they each have different requirements for illumination, most of them can be grown satisfactorily under less favourable conditions of light. Their lighting regime is really a question of adaptation: *C. cordata* and *C. griffithii* thrive better in the shade than in the light; the same can be said of *C. haerteliana* from Singapore. Their soil require-

ments are also modest: a layer (not less than 10 cm deep) of coarse sand mixed with loam and well washed peat suits them all. For the larger plants some ordinary garden soil can be added. They grow best in slightly acid water. The optimum temperature is around 20°C and can be increased to 30°C during the flowering season.

Lemna. Family Lemnaceae. Commonly found throughout the world. They are minute floating plants (known as Duckweeds), made up of a single leaf and a tiny root, that spread spontaneously at an amazing speed. Some (for example, the Ivy Duckweed, *L. trisulca*) are quite decorative; however, they are not recommended because they tend to invade the whole surface area of a tank, and they are difficult to eradicate, once they have been introduced to water. The same goes for the species of *Wolffia* which closely resemble *Lemna*.

Eichornia azurea. (Tropical and subtropical regions of America.) *E. crassipes* (hot regions of America), *Pontederia cordata* (hot regions of America). They are extremely attractive species of the family Pontederiaceae which float on stems made of spongy tissue which is filled with air. They have a rich display of soft spikes thickly covered with bright blue flowers (hence the common name

Lemna minor a small, floating plant.

'water hyacinth'). They increase by runners. They can be grown only in large aquaria as they need plenty of room. They also need illumination or sunlight and not too hard water.

Heteranthera. Family Pontederiaceae – America. Plants suited to temperate and warm aquaria, requiring water which is slightly soft or soft. *Heteranthera graminea* (from South America to the West Indies). It has strictly lanceolate leaves, often floating, needs a good light but not direct sunlight, and a sandy soil. It is the only species in this genus that grows in cold aquaria, but it is not popular as it tends to spread beyond control.

H. zosterifolia (tropical America). The submerged leaves are without stalks, lanceolate with straight edges, and a vivid light green colour; the floating leaves have stalks and are oblong and are rarely formed in aquarium specimens. It does not grow in hard water. It grows best in a soil of sand mixed with loam, with lighting from above, and a temperature of 20° to 28°C.

H. reniformis (hot regions of America). Its submerged leaves are lanceolate, with straight sides, but the others which are kidney-shaped either grow above the water, or float. It is reared only as young plants submerged in shallow water, with plenty of light; it needs soft water, 18° to 26°C.

Heleocharis acicularis. Family Ciperaceae – Found in Asia Minor, tropical zones of America, as well as sandy marshes of the northern temperate zone. The plant is submerged with finely branched stalks from 3 to 10 cm. It is popular because it does not need special attention; it grows well on sandy soil with a good light, and its runners soon spread to form a thick growth resembling grass at the bottom of the aquarium. It is extremely useful to fishes as they like to deposit their eggs on it. It also grows well during the winter although it is necessary to choose plants from the tropics for aquaria that are heated. The related species *H. prolifera* withstands hotter temperatures.

Sansevieria. Family Agavaceae – Africa. The species of this genus are well known and popular as indoor plants. The leaves are spade-shaped, fleshy and stiff, either growing straight or curved, dark green and often cut by vertical (sometimes horizontal) yellow bands. This plant is popular as it does not rely upon special light and needs little watering. However it can be cultivated equally well submerged in temperate or warm water aquaria, where it grows slowly and is durable. Similarly it is possible to grow plants not normally aquatic, as, for example, species of the genus *Dracaena*.

43

Animal Life in Relationship to Water

AQUATIC ANIMALS

The animal world of the seas and all the fresh waters of the earth is rich in numbers of species and has many variations of forms and habits, all of which make it as amazing to us as life on dry land. We all know how terrestrial animal and plant life seems to have survived and triumphed against all odds, and in the face of the most inhospitable conditions, and how, in response to these, morphological and physiological changes have occurred in the course of a long period of evolution. The same may be said about aquatic organisms. These can be divided into two main classes: marine and freshwater. Contrary to what one might be led to believe by superficial appearances, the dividing line between the two is not marked, and — as we shall see later on — the study of fishes proves it. Next, it is useful, perhaps, to point out some fundamental differences between terrestrial life in general, in order to appreciate more fully some important characteristics of creatures found on land and in water. First of all, though, let us remember that a solid base, used as a means upon which to rest or move, is not an exclusive characteristic of 'terrestrial' creatures; there are, in fact, many thousands of aquatic organisms that are firmly attached to solid bases, at the bottom of waters of various kinds. Much more important is the difference between the two elements surrounding them: air in one case, water in the other. Each of these elements exerts a vital influence upon the animals' powers as regards movement, breathing, feeding and reproduction.

Unlike the terrestrial animal, the aquatic animal (sponges and corals, for instance) can remain firmly attached to the sea-bed, and take food from the surrounding flowing water. Furthermore, even in aquatic animals which need to move to find their food the effort required is reduced to a minimum due to the animal's buoyancy in the denser medium of water. A crab, for instance, finds it much easier to swim, than to walk on dry land. With regard to respiration (taking in oxygen with the production of carbon dioxide), the basic process remains the same, however this time the roles are reversed: the terrestrial organism lives 'immersed' in air, the aquatic animal has to filter the oxygen dissolved in the water — which has less oxygen than dry air — for its needs. Many aquatic animals, especially the smaller and more simply organized kinds absorb oxygen through their skins; the rest have gills, which are special respiratory organs varying considerably in forms and position,

Opposite page: *Chaetodon speculum.* Butterfly-fishes are unmistakable for their distinctive bright coloration.

45

An example of a strange-looking tropical coral. Aquatic creatures, unlike terrestrial animals, can live attached to an underwater base, feeding on substances brought to them by the water.

according to the type of animal. The terms 'lungs' and 'gills', therefore, respectively indicate the major differences in the evolutionary adaptation of animals to the world of land and sea. Numerous animals living in the sea, rivers, and lakes produce a great number of eggs shed freely into the water into which the fertilizing cells are also shed. Eggs, larvae and young stages in various phases of development are able to disperse themselves easily and quickly into places where the water is suitable for their particular requirements with respect to temperature and salinity. An eminent zoologist once wrote: 'Water is by far the greatest animal nursery on earth; land belongs to a chosen minority . . .'; correctly interpreted, these words suggest that aquatic species are far more numerous and more varied than terrestrial animals, and we dare to add that they are easily the most ancient, for the earliest forms of life developed in the sea, and that terrestrial forms originated from aquatic ancestors.

From time immemorial, mankind has looked upon the oceans, rivers and lakes as a main source of food and raw material. A rich documentation, meant to spread the knowledge of animals to all those who love natural beauty, and consider aquaria as a valuable means of greater appreci-

ation, has been gradually added to a vast complex of scientific researches and technical know-how. The questions asked are: which animals live in water; which ones, amongst them, can find a comfortable home in an aquarium — big or small — and can enable us to observe the structure and habits of aquatic life. People lacking a particularly deep knowledge of natural science cannot possibly imagine just how vast the animal world is — i.e. how many species there are — and may be led to think that 'aquarium' species are many, but, in fact, there are relatively very few. Let us not forget first of all that both salt and fresh waters are the birth-place of a vast quantity of micro-organisms — animal (such as Protozoa) and vegetable (diatoms, peridinians) — that have a vital place in the 'food chain', because they provide a diet for many larger animals. An occasional look through a microscope would give us a fair idea of this fascinating microcosm. All the main groups of animals are represented in the aquatic world. First of all come the vertebrates, mainly fishes which we will discuss in detail later, but also members of other classes. Amphibians are strictly confined to water in which they live during the first stage of their development, but they do not inhabit the

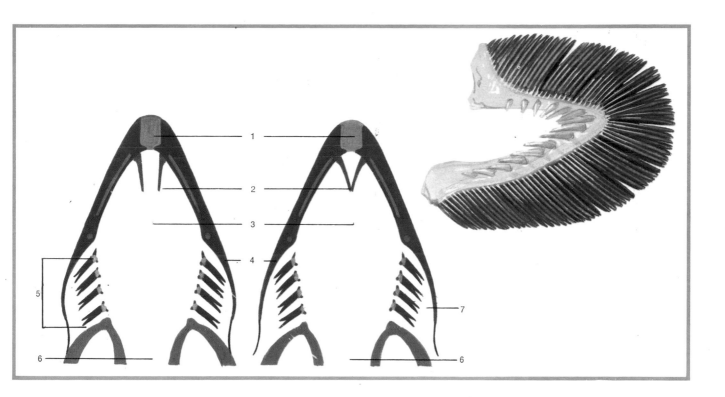

marine world, unlike reptiles. The sea snakes (not to be confused with the legendary sea serpents), turtles, and some crocodiles, are found in salt water together with some big lizards, as well. Then we have to consider the so-called 'water-birds': this is not a complete misnomer if we think of the habits of penguins or cormorants and other more common water-birds, such as geese and ducks. Some mammals, for example otters, are well adapted to life in water; others, such as seals and sea-lions and cetaceans, even more so, and this is why dolphins and whales are often thought of as fishes by some people.

As might be expected, the invertebrates (that is, those animals which do not have an internal bony skeleton — a term used for all animals other than vertebrates — are much more numerous and varied than the vertebrates.

Apart from a few arachnids (mites and spiders) we will dwell mainly on insects and crustaceans, i.e. arthropods (animals with jointed limbs) which have many aquatic species. Here we have a definite contrast: insects — so plentiful and forever present in all land environment — contribute only a little toward the numbers of fresh-water animals, and virtually nothing towards the marine fauna. Crustaceans, on the other hand, are found

in an incredible variety of forms and sizes everywhere in the aquatic world, in oceans as well as in rivers and lakes — they go from some almost microscopic copepods to the gigantic Japanese crab (*Macrocheira*).

Organisms of varied shapes have for a long time been put under the common name 'worms', a term that now lacks any scientific precision. Other important components of the marine fauna are bryozoans, and polychaete and nemertine worms, as well as other groups which are difficult to classify (because of differences of opinions amongst scientists). Molluscs are, however, a well-known family, with many aquatic species, mostly living in the sea. The seas are the only places inhabited by echinoderms — creatures of great beauty and which are extremely numerous — and the delicate ctenophores which have a transparent jelly-like body similar to that of the jellyfishes. There are some freshwater species representative of the coelenterates (such as *Hydra* and small jellyfishes) and the sponges (*Porifera*) such as *Spongilla*.

This summary, although very brief, will give some idea of the enormous variety of aquatic fauna, from which specimens can be chosen which are not only suitable for the aquarium, but which will enhance and beautify it.

Left: Diagram of the respiratory system of a fish with bony skeleton: 1 mouth; 2 valve-mechanism of mouth; 3 pharynx; 4 gill cover or operculum; 5 gills; 6 oesophagus; 7 gill chamber.
When the operculum is closed and the valve in the mouth (2) is open, the mouth is opened for the intake of water.
When the operculum is opened and the valve (2) is in a 'closed' position, the water is pushed through the gill and expelled.
Top right: Gill arch and gills of a fish with cartileginous skeleton.

47

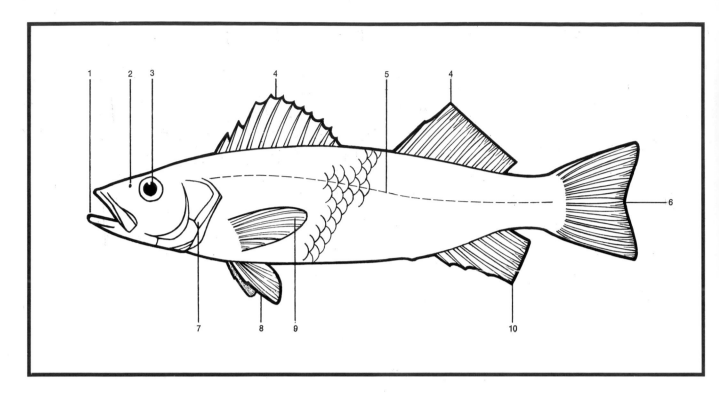

FISH

Many people who are not naturalists tend to apply the word 'fish' to most aquatic creatures and to group under one name a vast variety of organisms, including dolphins, octopuses and sponges. The true fish has a bony skeleton (backbone, skull, etc.); it breathes through gills, and uses fins as a means of propulsion. Furthermore, fishes are equipped with true jaws and their nostrils are set at each side of the head, unlike the cyclostomes (lampreys, hag fishes), which were once also regarded as fishes.

The characteristic fish-form is a spindle-shaped body, more or less compressed at the sides and gradually tapering at the rear into a narrow caudal peduncle which ends in the tail fin. There are, however, many variations and fishes can look like snakes, ribbons, discs, boxes etc. No less varied is the range of lengths and weights they can attain: while there exist fish less than 1 cm in length (some gobies, for example), there are others which reach enormous proportions (several metres in length and a few tons in weight, as in the case of the Basking Shark and Whale Shark). Some fishes (the Moray eel, for example have a naked (scaleless) skin, but generally, the body of a fish is covered by a layer of scales which

can differ in size and are commonly arranged in an overlapping pattern, rather like tiles on a roof. Scales can either be round-edged and smooth (cycloid), or rough and prickly on the free edge (ctenoid). Characteristic of the sharks and rays, and a few of their relatives, are the placoid scales, which are like small teeth, are not overlapped, and give these animals skins which are rough to the touch. On the other hand, the shiny apperance of some freshwater African fishes, like the bichirs, is due to a glossy layer of ganoine covering their scales, which are then known as ganoid scales. Coloration is an important detail in the life of fish. As a rule, they are much darker on the upper part of the body. Pigments of different kinds (carotenids, and others) contribute to their distinctive appearance, which can be quite impressive, especially in the case of many handsome tropical species. A special substance called guanine gives many fishes their characteristic silvery sheen.

Along each side (flank) of many fishes a distinct line, the 'lateral line', can often be seen. It marks the course of a series of canals containing sense organs which open through a small pore (or several pores) in the scales; sometimes this line is broken, at others it is found only on the anterior part of

External structure of a bony fish: 1 mouth; 2 nostrils; 3 eye; 4 dorsal fin; 5 lateral; 6 caudal fin; 7 gill cover (operculum); 8 pelvic fin; 9 pectoral fin; 10 anal fin line.

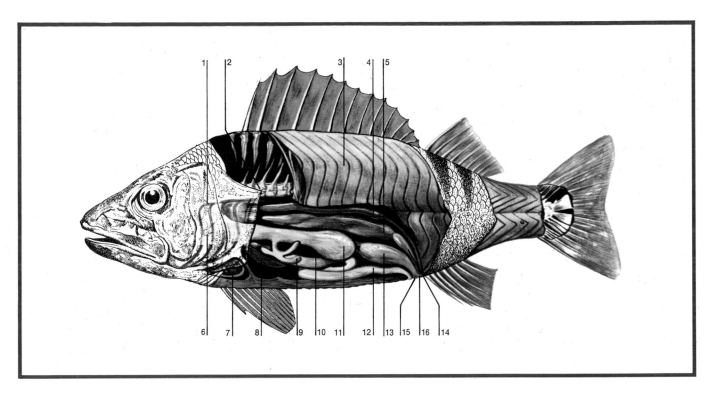

the body. Fish with cartilaginous skeletons, such as sharks and rays, have skin-covered fins, but the majority, represented by the bony fishes, have fins made up by a series of slender bones (sometimes spiny, otherwise flexible), disposed in the shape of a fan and held together by a membrane. A distinction is made between unpaired fins (dorsal, anal and caudal), and paired fins (pectoral and pelvic): they differ a great deal in their shape and sometimes their position according to the individual species.

The skeleton of a fish can either be completely cartilaginous or be ossified in varying degrees. The cranium has a complicated structure, with a great number of bones; to the vertebral column are attached the ribs. There is a remarkable series of muscle blocks (myomeres) running along each side of the body, and their distribution and location have a direct bearing on the flexibility of the body.

The gills are the respiratory organs. They consist of a fringe of respiratory lamellae, supported on bony arches and housed in a gill chamber each side of the fish's head. Rays and sharks have more than one set of gill chambers, gills and gill slits, each side. All other fishes have a single pair and the gill chambers and slits are protected by a thin, bony flap (operculum)

attached to the skull on one side and thus movable. The abdominal cavity contains the usual digestive, excretory and reproductive organs, which have an outlet on the undersurface of the fish, in front of the anal fin.

Many fish also possess a swim-bladder. This consists of a long slender sac (sometimes connected to the oesophagus [or gut]) which contains gas and is capable of expansion or contraction to counteract changes of pressure as the fish rises or sinks in the water. The circulation is generally of a simple type with blood carried by veins to the heart whence it is pumped to the gills and directly on to the muscles and organs; the red corpuscles are oval and have a nucleus. The nervous system includes a well-developed brain, spinal cord and numerous nerves amongst them those which run to the lateral line.

Fish comprise the great majority of species and individuals of all aquatic vertebrates and are found in all types of waters, from fresh to very salty. They are extremely adaptable animals and are therefore well able to survive and even thrive in practically any type of aquatic environmental condition. They are poikilothermic, i.e. they adjust their body temperature to that of the surrounding water. The swimming ability of fish ranges from the lazy

Internal structure of a bony fish: 1 dorsal; 2 vertebra; 3 myomeres; 4 kidney; 5 swim-bladder; 6 gills; 7 heart; 8 liver; 9 pyloric aorta caeca; 10 spleen; 11 stomach; 12 intestine; 13 gonads; 14 urinary bladder; 15 anus; 16 genital aperture.

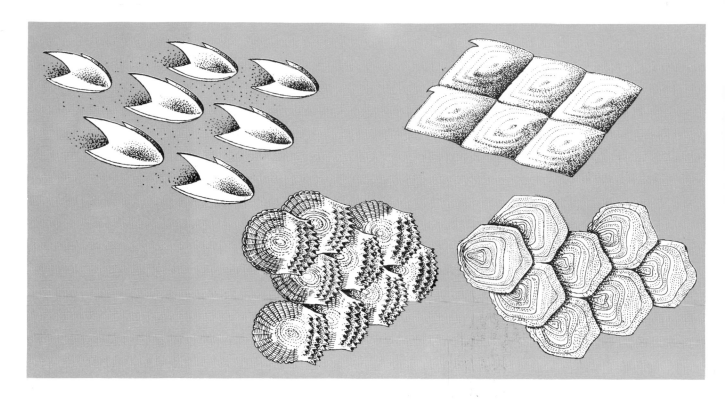

sluggishness of some tropical bottom-dwellers (e.g. the Frogfish) to the extreme swiftness of the fast ocean-swimmers (e.g. the Swordfish). Propulsion is normally obtained by flexion of the body from side to side, which causes the fins to swing from side to side—particularly the tail fin, which provides the main forward thrust (and acts as a rudder).

Generally the diet consists of other animals, and apart from some herbivorous species (e.g. the Mediterranean Sea Bream, *Salpa*) a large number are fierce predators. In some cases the minute organisms in the plankton play a fundamental role, but in other cases debris of various kinds scattered at the bottom of the water provides food. As we all know, many fish live in fresh water but they are more numerous in the sea. According to a recent survey, 41% of the total is made up by freshwater fishes. In all, there are at least 21,000 known species of fishes and new ones are continually being distinguished. The major division be-between marine and freshwater fishes is by no means well defined nor is it the only one: it is true that most common fishes seem to belong to either one of these two groups, but there are several subdivisions as well, within each group. Some species, as we know, periodically migrate (e.g.

Salmon) coming from the sea to breed in a river (anadromous) or vice versa (catadromous; for example, the freshwater Eel). Variation in salinity also makes for more distinctions, so the stenohaline fishes which require a fixed level of salt, differ from the euryhaline fishes which can tolerate water with a considerable degree of salinity—Grey Mullets for instance, are euryhaline. Ecological preferences of fishes for one particular environment must also be taken into account for their grouping: torrents, rivers and lakes all have their specific inhabitants. In the sea the coastal zone is populated by fishes different from those found in mid-water in the open sea, and from those living in the abyssal zone of the deep sea. The different types of sea-beds (rocks, sand or coral, etc.) are of great importance in the distribution of fishes, as also is the water temperature—some species are only found within the limits of a specific isotherm. The vertical distribution is also vast, as fishes reach incredible depths and have been seen living as low down as 10,000 metres and over, in the Pacific.

Some fish (e.g. Conger eels) lead a solitary life, while others (e.g. Sardines) are gregarious and live in schools throughout their lives, although some other individuals (e.g. Tuna) only join

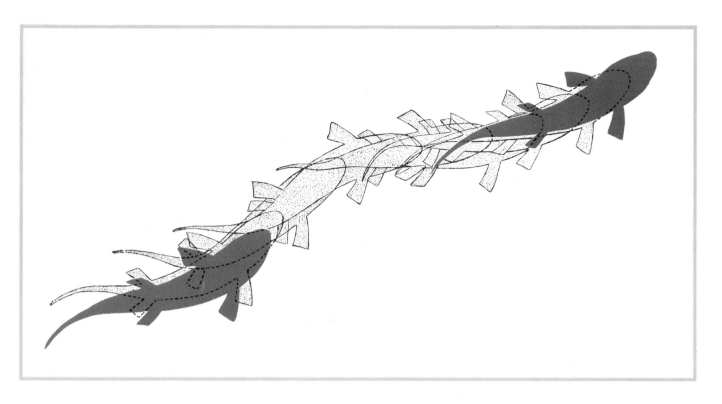

together at spawning time. The social relationships of fishes—both within species, and between them and invertebrate animals—are many: a series of characteristic associations have been known for a long time as for example with sea anemones and sea cucumbers. Many crustaceans (mainly copepods) are parasitic on fishes, and so are various kinds of helminths (trematodes etc.).

Most fishes reproduce by laying eggs that are fertilized outside their body. In some, however, the egg is fertilized internally, and these viviparous fishes include all the selachians (such as rays, sharks and their relatives) and some bony fishes (e.g. *Gambusia*). The sexes are distinct in almost all fishes, but some (sea perches, for instance) are hermaphrodite. In others, the male and female gonads develop in the same individual at different times: this phenomenon—occurring in the Gilt-head Bream, for instance—seems to be more common than it was first thought. Very often males and females differ from each other in size, colour and development of fins, and this phenomenon of sexual dimorphism is often very marked. Some fishes lay their eggs throughout the year, others only seasonally (usually in spring and summer). Associated with seasonal spawning are long-

distance migrations, an activity usually accompanied by interesting physiological (as well as morphological) changes, under hormonal control.

Sharks and other selachians have large eggs, but relatively few in number, with a large yolk rich in food for the developing embryo; in some cases, where a kind of placenta is formed, nourishment is supplied by the mother fish (as, for example, in some species of Smooth Hound). With few exceptions, all other fishes lay a great quantity of small eggs (1,200,000 in the Brill) and these can either float freely in the water, or drop to the bottom, or be attached to vegetation or shells etc. (according to individual species). The incubation period differs considerably from fish to fish, and in the post-embryonic stage may involve some striking metamorphosis. Highly characteristic are the larvae of eels (transparent and ribbon-like and known as leptocephali), flatfish larvae and larvae of the Sunfish (*Mola*). Parental care is often found in fishes. A proper nest is built by the male of the Three-spined Stickleback in which eggs are laid; some small fishes of the seashore lay their eggs in an empty shell, and the male Sea Horse incubates the eggs in a pouch on its upper tail. Some fishes living in fresh water and others

Fishes swim with a snake-like movement of the body, practically cutting their path through the water because it is incompressible. The water is displaced by the zig-zagging movement—especially of the caudal fin—parly aided by the spindle-shaped, hydrodynamically adapted, body of the fish. The body, too, moves from side to side, although in a less marked way.

51

An example of association between animals belonging to the two almost opposite extremes of the zoological spectrum; a sea anemone and a Clown fish (*Amphiprion*), living in tropical seas.

in the sea incubate their eggs in their mouths and do not feed while doing so. Fishes are vertebrates which can grow indefinitely, as they still grow after reaching sexual maturity, although at a somewhat reduced rate. External conditions — such as temperature and salinity of water — have a considerable influence on consumption of food, and consequently on their rate of growth. Growth rate can be evaluated by counting the concentric rings formed on the scales that mark the yearly growth. Generally male fish reach sexual maturity earlier than females.

The life-span of fishes varies considerably. Some very small species do not live more than a year — the smaller gobies are the most common example — while some other fishes can live half a century (e.g. Sturgeon). Hybrids between types of fishes are not a rarity, and they are very interesting. Normally their appearance is a fair mixture of the characteristics of the two parent species — often belonging to different genera (e.g. Carp and Crucian Carp). Hybrids can either be sterile or fertile and have a particular predominance of one or other sex.

When discussing the geographical distribution of fishes it is necessary to distinguish two major types — marine and freshwater. Some fresh-water fish belong to families whose members belong entirely to that environment (e.g. cyprinids, cichlids, etc.); others are freshwater representatives of mostly marine families (e.g. blennies, gobies). The composition of the fish fauna of the different continents is varied and comprises elements of both the above groups. In fact, while the Australian fish population is small and mostly composed of marine fish representatives in fresh water, we find an enormous number and range of fishes in the tropical regions of Asia, Africa and Central America, including some very colourful small species that have become famous among aquarists. The tropical waters of the Amazon are inhabited by Piranhas, Tetras, Corydoras etc.; while the very pretty carps (Danios, Rasboras etc.), and the well-known Fighting-fishes come from the Indo-Malaysian region. Of great interest are the fishes which live in the great lakes of Africa, the majority of which belong to the family Cichlidae. European freshwater fishes which are not particularly attractive, are closely related to those of the northern region of Central Asia. In several continents cave-dwelling fishes are known; they lack colour pigments, and are often blind.

Marine species often have a very

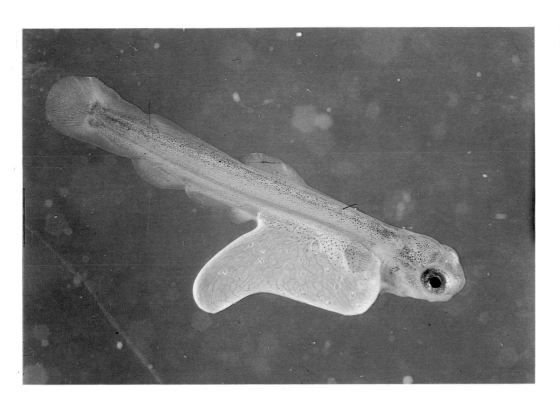

Top: larval stage of a trout in the first days of life.

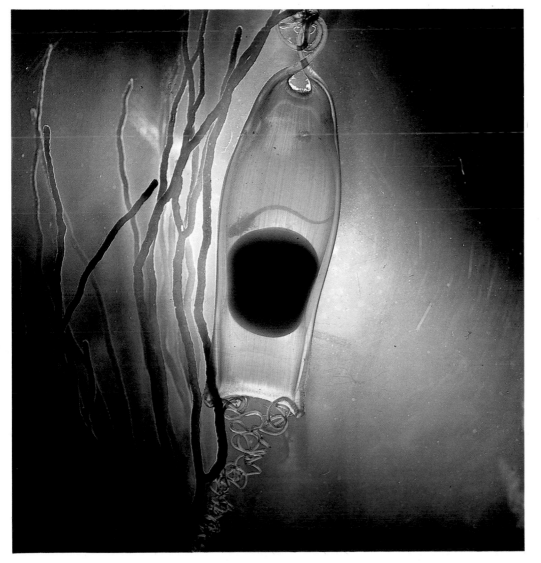

Bottom: Each egg of the Dogfish is enclosed in a characteristic transparent shell, through which the developing embryo can be seen together with the mass of yolk that serves as nourishment.

Eggs and embryos of
Hippocampus (Seahorse)
are kept by the male fish
in a ventral pouch during
incubation (top), until
the hatching of the
young (below).

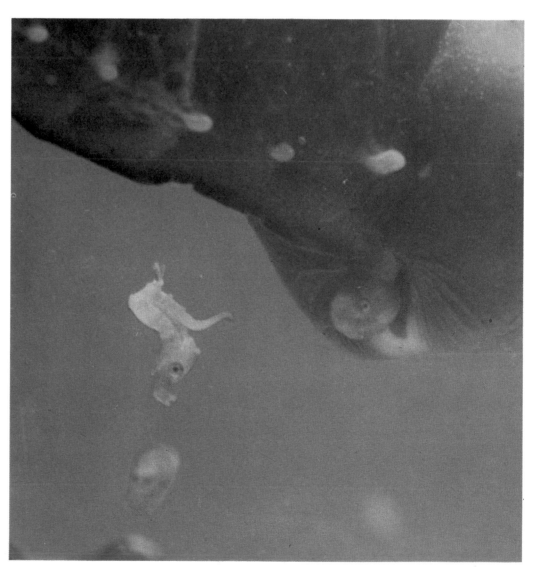

Large areas of the sea-bed can appear covered by the moving tentacles — capable of stinging — that belong to many individuals of big sea anemones.

restricted distribution, as for instance, some blennies and gobies, which are confined to the Mediterranean, or they may be distributed throughout all the oceans; cases of cosmopolitan distribution are not uncommon (e.g. the Swordfish and the Sunfish). There are, of course, intermediate situations where a species is moderately widespread. Leaving aside the fish population of the polar zones, we shall concentrate instead on the fishes of the Atlanto-Mediterranean basin as well as the Indo-Pacific fish fauna, all of which are contained within the warmest zones of the Earth. Most Mediterranean fishes are also found in the Atlantic, sometimes ranging as far as the American shores (e.g. Triggerfish). The term 'Indo-Pacific fishes' is applied to a very rich fish fauna living in the Red Sea and the Indian Ocean, and a more or less large section of the Pacific Ocean: i.e. in all the regions where the coral-reef formations are best developed to provide a suitable background for the most magnificent animal specimens. Some Indo-Pacific fishes have penetrated into the Mediterranean through the Suez Canal.

Fishes are by far the most numerous and varied of vertebrate animals, a factor connected with their ancient origin. Several species belonging to vastly different families can be traced back to an aquatic ancestor already living in the Devonian period — 300 million years ago. Apart from the cyclostomes — which have special characteristics of their own — all other fishes can be divided into two distinct classes — those with a cartilaginous skeleton (the selachians) and the bony fishes — irrespective of the fundamental differences of form, physiology or embryology existing among them. The first, smaller in number and mainly marine, have skin which is generally rough and covered in irregular rows with small placoid scales (dermal denticles). They usually have five gill chambers and gill slits on each side: they reproduce by internal fertilization and viviparous birth as a rule, although some species lay eggs. The second class contains fishes with only a single gill opening each side, covered by the bony operculum (gill cover); their skeletons are of varying degrees of ossification, and egg-laying is the rule. Bony fishes not only constitute the great majority of all known fishes, they include all the fishes of the greatest economic importance.

Variations of body features, often related to geographical distinction, occur within species and they help to distinguish subspecies which mostly are a result of isolation in an area leading to genetic isolation.

55

Freshwater Fishes

Acipenseridae. A family which is represented by a small number of species. They are often regarded as 'living fossils' on account of the many primitive features they share with fishes which are now known as fossils. Sturgeons are the best known members of the family, and are found in Europe, northern Asia, and North America. Some species live only in fresh water, while others — for example, the European Sturgeon (*Acipenser sturio*) — migrate from the sea to a river to breed; such migrations are termed anadromous. Sturgeons have a very distinctive appearance: series of bony plates run along their bodies; they have a short snout; a small tooth-less mouth, placed ventrally; the tail fin is asymmetric (similar to sharks), the upper lobe being longer. They can be very large: one species reaching 9 m in length and 1,300 kg in weight. Sturgeons feed on small animals and also vegetable matter. Eggs are deposited on the bottom and are numerous but small. The much appreciated caviar is, in fact, prepared from unshed sturgeon eggs. Their flesh is also popular as food, therefore Sturgeons are fished in various regions. Small to medium specimens are sometimes kept in public aquaria.

Amiidae. A family which is well known from several kinds of fossil fishes but the only surviving member is the Bowfin (*Amia calva*) found in rivers and lakes of North America. It grows to a length of 70 cm; it has cycloid scales, a long dorsal fin, and other fins rounded without spines. It has a honeycombed swim-bladder that helps it breathe air. It is plain brown in colour but males have a round black spot edged with red at the base of the tail fin. The eggs are laid during the night in a nest prepared by the male in amongst the vegetation and the male remains in sole charge of the eggs and young.

Lepisosteidae. The Garpikes deserve the name of 'living fossils' as much as the Sturgeons and the Bowfin. The few living species have a long narrow snout, sharp strong teeth, shiny, very heavy scales and a swim-bladder similar in form and function to that of the Bowfin. Garpikes live in the rivers and lakes of North and Central America; they are voracious predators, living mainly on fish. The best known is the *Lepisosteus osseus*, or Long-nose Gar, widely distributed in the United States: it is up to 150 cm long, olive grey with black spots. Because of their size these fishes are only suitable for large public aquaria.

Salmonidae. The Salmon and Trout are well-known members of this important family, typical of the temperate

Opposite page: A tropical freshwater aquarium.

Top right: A Sturgeon
(genus *Acipenser*). This
large fish has an
unmistakable appearance.
Bottom left: The European
Trout (*Salmo trutta*) which
may vary in size and colour.

Opposite page:
Top right: A Pike (*Esox
lucius*) one of the best
known members of the
European fish fauna.
Centre right: A Rainbow
Trout (*Salmo gairdneri*).
This species was originally
imported from North
America and is now found
in other continents.
Bottom right: Brook Charr
(*Salvelinus fontinalis*).

zone of the northern hemisphere, and
widely found in the arctic regions. All
salmonids have an elongate body with
small cycloid scales, and strong teeth
as one might expect of carnivorous
fishes. The fins are without spines and
they have a typical adipose fin placed
on the back just before the tail. The
swim-bladder is well developed and
is connected to the oesophagus.
Coloration is quite varied – even within
the same species – therefore salmonids
are attractive in aquaria. While some
spend all their lives in freshwater
(rivers or lakes, according to preference), other species make seasonal
migrations and are anadromous as are
the Sturgeons. The eggs are relatively
large and are deposited usually in
gravel in small hollows made by
driving the body and fins in the river
bed. In the anadromous species the
young migrate to the sea after a while,
and grow there until they reach sexual
maturity, when they make their way
upriver again to spawn. All salmonids
are carnivorous and feed on small
fishes and invertebrates. Their culi-
nary value is well known, as the flesh
tastes extremely good; amongst the
best of edible freshwater fishes. The
best known of salmonids is, of course,
the Salmon (*Salmo salar*), males may
grow to 1·5 m and weigh up to 36 kg,
while females are smaller. The body is

silver-grey with black spots. This handsome fish is not found in the Mediterranean, but is widely distributed in the North Atlantic both along the European, Greenland and North American coasts. Due to various obstacles (river pollution, construction of dams etc.), the numbers of Salmon have been greatly reduced. The Trout (*S. trutta*) is very similar to the Salmon, but is more variable and only migrates when living in rivers on the Atlantic coastline of Europe and in the Black Sea. In Italy and other Mediterranean regions one finds 'torrent' and 'lake' populations. The torrent type are small (20 to 30 cm) with red and black spots; the lake trout are much larger (over 1 m and 10 kg) without the red spots. Trout breed in autumn and winter, and lake trout will then enter rivers to spawn.

The best known American trout is the Rainbow Trout (*S. gairdneri*) which was introduced into Europe towards the end of the last century and is now abundant. It is easily identified by its dense black spots and the rainbow-hued stripe along its sides.

The Charrs (genus *Salvelinus*) differ from trout in having smaller scales and different teeth formation. They are also well coloured and are therefore suitable as attractive aquarium fishes. However, they are mainly of

interest to fishermen as their flesh is extremely good to eat. The Charrs can be reared in hatcheries, too. The true Alpine Charr (*Salvelinus alpinus*) is in fact limited to a very limited zone of the Alps (Trentino up to 2,300 m) but its overall geographical distribution is immensely vast, because it is a world-wide species, with non-migratory and migratory types. Its coloration becomes vivid during the breeding season (October to January), when the underside becomes red; the white edged fins are characteristic. The Brook Charr (*S. fontinalis*) is indigenous to North America, but has been introduced elsewhere; only limited success has been achieved in the British Isles where it has been introduced. It is readily identified by the green and yellowish-white variegations along its back and sides. The Charrs prefer cool well-oxygenated water, as do all salmonids.

Some ichthyologists prefer to include the Grayling and Whitefishes within this family, others separate them into Thymallidae and Coregonidae.

Esocidae. This is a family consisting of several species of Pike one of which (*Esox lucius*) is found in Europe and many parts of northern Asia and North America (where it is known as the Northern Pike). The Pike has a very long body (females grow to 1·5 m), greenish in colour with silvery-white stripes and spots; a snout rather like the mouth of a crocodile, and well-developed strong teeth. These characteristic fish live in rivers, lakes and even ponds, especially where the vegetation is rich. The Pike is carnivorous and voracious; it hunts its prey by lurking amongst the vegetation (to which it also attaches its eggs) and then hurling itself after its prey. It seems that the Pike can live up to thirty years, but there has been much exaggeration about its longevity. In an aquarium no species of pike can be mixed with other fishes of a size likely to become its victims.

Pantodontidae. One of the most typical and strange African fish is the small *Pantodon buchholzi*, the only species of its family. It only grows to about 10 cm and is famous for its large wing-like pectoral fins and smaller thread-like pelvic fins, which extend as isolated rays free of the membrane. It is olive-brown with spots and stripes of a darker shade or deep yellow. This singular small fish lives in Africa, particularly in the rivers of Nigeria, Cameroon and Zaire; it keeps near the surface, as a rule, but leaps out now and again. Because of this habit, it has also been called (without much foundation) a 'freshwater flying fish'. It feeds on small animals. Its eggs

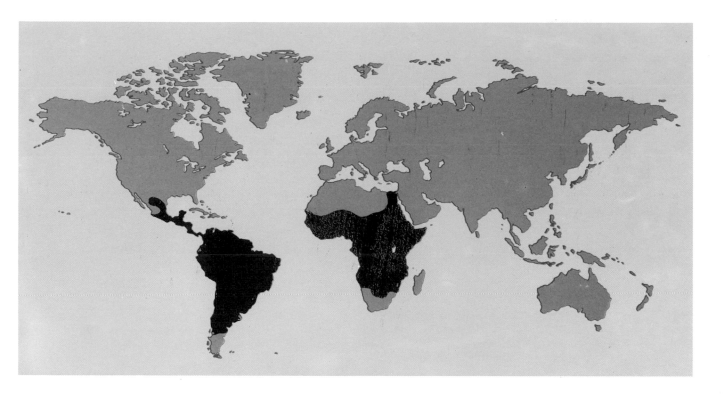

float and are relatively large. The term *Pantodon* ('all-teeth') is due to its unusually well developed set of teeth, which line the palate and tongue, as well as its jaws.

Notopteridae. Fish with a characteristic outline of the body—very compressed—deep towards the head and tapering almost to a point at the tail; the dorsal fin is either small or altogether absent, the anal fin, by contrast, is well developed and continues along most of the underside of the fish. These fishes live in tropical fresh water. The best known are the species of *Notopterus* of southern Asia and the Malayan archipelago. *N. chitala* is widely distributed; in some Indian rivers it can grow to over 1 m in length. The eggs are deposited on the bottom mud and closely guarded by the male. In the western region of tropical Africa there is *N. afer*, also called 'Lolembe' by the Congolese. Also found in Africa is *Xenomystus nigri*, measuring about 20 cm, and differing from *Notopterus* by lacking a dorsal fin. Because of the shape of their bodies, these fishes are often called Knifefishes. In aquaria they require high temperatures (24° to 28°C).

Characidae. This is a large family of fishes, which includes a great number of species widely distributed in tropical Africa and Central and South America.

The characins usually have well-developed teeth of different form, according to species, close-set scales covering the body, and fins without bony spines. They have a small adipose fin placed on the back close to the tail fin. The presence of this fin and the fact that their jaws have teeth distinguishes them from the members of the Carp family (Cyprinidae). Both families have 'weberian ossicles'—consisting of a chain of bones (elements of the first few vertebrae), which connects the swim-bladder to the inner ear. Characins are very varied in looks, size and colours: the numerous smaller species are amongst the best known and most popular fishes for aquaria, and come mainly from South America.

The Neon Tetra (*Hyphessobrycon innesi*) is quite famous: it only measures a few centimetres and has a vivid blue band on each side. It is easy to keep in the aquarium, where it will breed. It originated from the far west of the Amazon region. A similarly pretty species is *H. callistus* which is widely found in Brazilian rivers and is very varied both for the colour of its body (reddish pink) and for the markings of black dots on its sides and on the fins; as a rule it has a marked black spot on its dorsal fin. Many other small and beautiful fishes are

Map showing the distribution of the family Characidae.

61

known in the genus *Hemigrammus* — this name means 'an incomplete lateral line'. Amongst them, the *H. ocellifer* (Amazon and Guyana) is easily recognized by the almost luminous yellow spot placed over a black one on its caudal peduncle. *Pristella riddlei*, a small South American species has black and white spots on its dorsal and anal fins, and is a common inhabitant of aquaria.

Thayeria sanctaemariae (Brazil) and *Gymnocorymbus ternetzi* (Brazil and Paraguay) are slightly smaller species, but easily identified. The first has a well-marked black band on its sides, extending along the lower lobe of the tail fin. *Gymnocorymbus* has a narrow flattened body and well-developed anal fin. The front half of the sides are lighter — i.e. grey crossed by two black vertical bands, while the other half and the dorsal and anal fins are blackish. All these small characins are gregarious and carnivorous. As they are definitely tropical species, they require rather warm water and, given ideal conditions, they breed in aquaria without difficulty. They are part of that rich South American fauna, which attracted the first explorers but which still remains relatively unknown.

Spread throughout South America is *Astyanax fasciatus*, often called the Banded Astyanax, up to 11 cm in

Above: The much feared Piranha of South American rivers belongs to the genus *Serrasalmus*.
Left: The Serpae Tetra (*Hyphessobrycon serpae*), one of the prettiest of the South American characins.

Opposite page: Top left: Cardinal Tetra (*Cheirodon axelrodi*). Top right: Lemon Tetra (*Hyphessobrycon pulchripinnis*). Centre left: Three-banded Pencil Fish (*Nannostomus trifasciatus*). Centre right: Striped Anostomus (*Anostomus anostomus*). Bottom: the Neon Tetra (*Hyphessobrycon innesi*); this fish is considered an aquarist's jewel, with full justification.

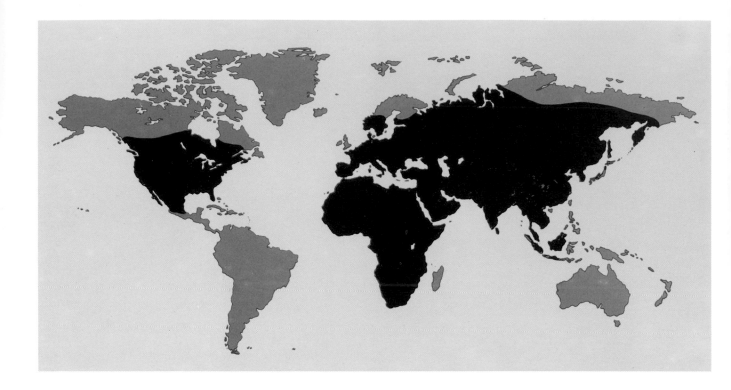

A map showing the
distribution of the family
Cyprinidae.

length, adorned with a silver stripe on each side and a black spot at the base of the tail. It is remembered especially because of its similarity with the Blind Cave-fish (*Anoptichthys jordani*). This fish was discovered in a Mexican cave and is about 10 cm long, pinkish white, sometimes almost transparent. It is blind, as are most cave-dwellers. However, it will live in aquaria, even in normal light and it feeds on debris and crumbs found at the bottom. Few of the freshwater fishes of South America have gained the same notoriety as the Piranhas which are rather large characins (they reach 50 cm), named thus by the Tupí-Guaraní Indians. They have a very deep laterally flattened body; the belly with a series of small tooth-like scales forming a sharp keel; short snout and powerful jaws, with pointed and sharp triangular teeth. A number of species are recognized within the genus *Serrasalmus*. They differ in details of form and colour as well as geographical distribution and degree of aggression. The most feared is the largest: *S. piraya*, of the eastern zones of Brazil (the basin of the Rio San Francisco). The Piranhas are extremely dangerous, as they attack any man or animal that happens to be wading across the river and quickly devour them, leaving only a few bones:

their habitual diet is, however, smaller fishes. Although true Piranhas, of limited size, are kept in aquaria, it is more common to see in captivity smaller characins—as, for example those belonging to the genus *Metynnis*, which bear a certain resemblance to Piranhas. Very unlike the Piranha, on account of its small mouth and few teeth, is the species *Leporinus fasciatus*; up to 20 cm in length, with a series of about ten black rings across its body, it is found between Guyana and Uruguay. *Nannostomus trifasciatus* is more colourful: it comes from the Amazon regions and has sticky eggs that cling to plants or to the sides of the aquarium. One of the aquarium characins with an interesting method of reproduction is *Copeina arnoldi* (Brazil). The female fish leaps out of the water and lays the eggs on a dry surface—the sides of an aquarium, for instance—perhaps to keep them safe from possible predators; the male then sprays them periodically with its tail to keep them damp, until the fry emerge and fall off into the water. Sometimes it takes about seventy hours before the eggs hatch. This fish grows to 10 cm in length. Characins are well represented amongst the African fish fauna but the species are generally larger and less colourful than the American ones.

However, the *Nannaethiops unitaeniatus* (Nile, Niger and Zaire) is worth mentioning. It is small and has a brown stripe going along its side, parallel to a golden-yellow one above it.

A particular group of small characins are the so-called Hatchet fishes (*Gasteropelecus*, *Carnegiella*) from South America, which have a deep flat belly distended in an arch.

Cyprinidae. This is probably the most numerous family of fishes. It contains some thousand species, relatively uniform in their overall shape, and often endowed with beautiful coloration which makes them very attractive as aquarium specimens. They differ from characins in that they have no teeth in the jaws and no adipose dorsal fin: they have, instead, one or more rows of teeth on a pair of bones in the pharynx (known as the pharyngeal teeth). Often they have one or two pairs of sensory barbels around the mouth. The scales are cycloid (i.e. smooth edged), and the fins generally lack spiny rays. The swim-bladder is well developed and divided by a narrow passage into two successive chambers, the anterior one of which is connected to the oesophagus.

The cyprinids are perhaps the most typical freshwater fishes. They are more or less omnivorous, the food being crushed against a hard pad in the roof of the throat by the teeth of the movable pharyngeal bones. During the breeding season some species have colour variations or little white blisters (spawning tubercles) appearing on their body (especially over the head) and fins. They frequently crossbreed with other cyprinid fishes, even different genera. This group of fishes has an immense area of distribution, including Europe, Asia, Africa and North America. Cyprinids have held the first place in the list of aquarium fishes for many years, particularly several tropical Asian species. The family takes its name from the scientific name of the well-known Carp (*Cyprinus carpio*). The Carp is a large fish (over 1 m in length and weighs 30 kg), with two pairs of short barbels on the upper lip, and a rather long dorsal fin which begins with a long, stout, spiny ray, as does the anal fin. It has an olive-brown back and golden-yellow sides. The Carp originates from the Danube and Black Sea basins, but has been imported into all other continents, and it is now one of the most widespread freshwater fishes found in temperate zones of both hemispheres. The eggs (200 to 700,000) are attached to the vegetation. The Carp is polymorphic—i.e. it varies greatly in the shape of the

The Mirror Carp is easily identified by the few but large scales on its body.

65

The photographs reproduced on this page show a few varieties of the best known ornamental fish; the Goldfish (*Carassius auratus*) which originated in Asia.

body (in some cases being long, in others short but deep bodied), as well as in the formation of the scales. Some may have only a few large scales as in the case of the so-called Mirror Carp, or be completely scaleless, as is the Leather Carp. The King Carp on the other hand has scales all over its body.

Carassius auratus is the well-known Goldfish, usually looked upon as being the most banal aquarium species. It is akin to the Carp, but has no barbels and is smaller, very rarely growing beyond 30 cm in length. The original home of the Goldfish is Asia. The coloration of these fishes is very varied (red, yellow, orange, white; with or without black spots); it may have a very large tail fin (e.g. the Comet) or be scaleless (e.g. Shubunkin); or it can have eyes with an upward setting, and altogether look like a monster. This species is very similar to the Crucian Carp (*C. carassius*), which is widely distributed in various European and Asian regions. The Crucian Carp cross-breeds with the Carp to produce a hardy, fastgrowing hybrid.

The Barbs constitute a major branch of the cyprinids, with fishes of different shapes and colours, many of which have two pairs of barbels, others have none; the first ray in the dorsal fin is often strong and spiny. The most widely distributed in European rivers are the Barbels (*Barbus barbus*) and in Europe only *B. meridionalis*. The first is bigger (up to 60 cm in length) and has the spine in the dorsal fin stout; while the second species has a slender dorsal spine and the body and fins are covered with brown-black marks.

Much more interesting, from the aquarist's point of view, are the tropical species, especially those from Asia. *B. titteya* is a small, graceful species from Ceylon that can be identified by a longitudinal black stripe along each side, and *B. nigrofasciatus* has delicate tinges of red and brown. A larger species and one which is much sought after, is *B. everetti*, a native of Malaya, which is golden yellow with a few large brown spots. The Fivebanded Barb (*B. pentazona*) is found from Thailand to Borneo; it is a small silvery-gold cyprinid with broad, dark, vertical bands, similar to its Malayan relative, the Tiger Barb (*B. tetrazona*). The classification of tropical Barbs is still far from complete, but they are easy to maintain in aquaria and some can be bred without trouble, laying their eggs on the bottom or on plants. They prefer an environment rich in plants in amongst which they love to roam in shoals when living in their

Top: The Italian Barbel (*Barbus barbus plebejus*).
Top right: The Italian Vairone (*Leuciscus souffia muticellus*).
Bottom right: The Italian Chub (*Leuciscus cephalus cabeda*).

67

Left: A small school of
Bleak (*Alburnus alburnus*),
a species of cyprinid fish
widely distributed
throughout Europe.
Right top: Another cyprinid
fish, the southern European
form of Roach (*Rutilus
rubilio*); bottom: The Tiger
Barb (*Barbus tetrazona*)
a small Asian species.

Opposite page: Top left:
The White Cloud Mountain
Minnow (*Tanichthys
albonubes*), a small Chinese
cyprinid.
Right: The Zebra fish
(*Danio revio*), which is
well known and easily
recognizable in the
aquarium.
Below: A golden variety
of *Barbus semifasciolatus*
which lives in China.

natural state. There are many other exotic species of cyprinid, amongst which are the Red-tailed Black Shark (*Labeo bicolor*) — the name of this genus refers to its very well developed lips. It possesses one or two pairs of short barbels and is completely black, with a contrasting red tail fin; it grows to 12 cm. This pretty cyprinid lives in the rivers of Thailand, together with the Black Shark (*Morulius chrysophekadion*), which is distributed widely as far as the Sunda Islands. This is a black or bluish-black fish, growing to a length of 60 cm.

One of the most widely distributed European cyprinid fishes is the Chub (*Leuciscus cephalus*), which is subdivided in several subspecies. One of these (*L. c. cabeda*) is found in Italy — where it is called Cavedano — and in some regions of France and Spain; it lives in lakes and rivers and adapts itself fairly easily to aquaria, but there it is likely to eat smaller fishes. It has a bluish-grey back and a shiny silvery tint on the side.

Another European species, but one not found in Britain is the Vairone (*L. souffia*) (in Italy it is represented by the subspecies *muticellus*) which belongs to the same genus and is easily identified: it has smaller and more numerous scales and a slate-grey or blackish stripe running along

each side. There are also at least two species of the genus *Rutilus*, characterized by a single row of pharyngeal teeth, as against the double rows as in the genus *Leuciscus*. The Triotto (*R. rubilio*), a fish related to the European Roach (*R. rutilus*) is commonly found in rivers and lakes all over Italy; it reaches 20 cm in length at the most and has a striped marking similar to *L. souffia*. The Orfe (*L. idus*) is found north of the Alps and is widely spread in eastern Europe and in the central and northern regions of Asia. It has a silvery-grey body with a brownish-grey back.

The Tench (*Tinca tinca*), which is usually plain greenish brown in colour becomes rather brighter at spawning time. It has a rather short thick body and an almost straight-edged tail fin: it grows to about 60 cm and over 6 kg. The Bleak (*Alburnus alburnus*) is a pretty little fish (maximum length 15 cm). Its name describes the uniformly silvery-white colouring of its body. It lives in rivers, less often in lakes, fairly near the surface of the water and feeds on plankton. Its eggs, however, are deposited at the bottom (sand or pebbles). It is very gregarious and often forms dense schools.

The Rudd (*Scardinius erythrophthalmus*) is larger than the Bleak and has a heavier, thicker body; it has red fins

(apart from the dorsal fin, which is brown). It is largely found all over Europe and Asia, in the most varied environments (rivers, lakes, ponds and marshes).

The members of the genus *Chondrostoma* are cyprinids characterized by the unusual position of their mouths on the underside; their lips are hard and horny, with sharp edges. Two species are common in Italy: *Chondrostoma toxostoma* (about 20 cm), with a brown band along each side; and *C. soetta* (up to 40 cm) with a plain silver body. Very similar species are also found in other European regions but none are native to Britain. The Minnow (*Phoxinus phoxinus*) is no longer than 12 cm. It has a short roundish snout, small scales; its lateral line is not distinct and is often restricted to the front half of the body. Its area of distribution consists of almost the entire European region (including the Alps to a height of 2,500 m and the Po Valley), and the northern parts of Asia. In the Alpine lakes it is often eaten by Trout, while feeding on Trout fry in its turn.

One of the most interesting European cyprinids is the Bitterling (*Rhodeus sericeus*), which grows to a length of 9 cm. It, too, has an interrupted lateral line; its body is flat and deep, with a longitudinal greenish-blue stripe

across each side. It lives in still waters or slow-flowing rivers with plentiful vegetation.

The Bitterling is a Eurasian species, the Bronze Bream (*Abramis brama*), a large cyprinid (it reaches 60 cm in length and weighs 3 kg) with a high-backed body of a uniform greeny-bronze colour is similarly distributed. Well-known aquarium species are the small Asian cyprinids belonging to the two genera *Danio* and *Rasbora*. Immediately recognizable is the Zebra Danio (*Danio rerio*), only a few centimetres long and endowed with alternate yellow and dark-blue stripes, running along each side of the body. It lives in the rivers of the eastern regions of India. Slightly bigger, but paler in colour (although bearing the same striped markings of yellow and blue) is the Giant Danio (*Danio malabaricus*) (India, Ceylon). These fishes are easy to rear; they do well at temperatures ranging from 18° to 24°C, and breed without difficulty. They have, in fact, a high rate of birth and a rapid growth. The Harlequin Fish (*Rasbora heteromorpha*) is 4 to 5 cm long, rosy-silver with a large triangular spot on each side of the tail-end of its body. It came originally from Thailand, the Malayan peninsula, and Sumatra. The tiny White Cloud Mountain Minnow (southern China)

is called *Tanichthys albonubes*; its maximum length is 4 cm; it has two striking black and yellow parallel lines along each side, and its tail fin is bright red at the base.

Cobitidae. In spite of sharing some of its characteristics with the Cyprinidae (i.e. the weberian ossicles), this family is entirely different and its members (the Loaches) — all of which live in European and Asian fresh water — have bodies which are always elongated and almost parallel in their outline. The mouth is small and surrounded by three pairs of barbels. The scales are small and the lateral line is more or less reduced. The Loaches are small and live on the bottom, or even buried and they are part of the benthos. Almost all the aquarium species originate in southern Asia and Indonesia. A widespread European species, which is confined to eastern England, is the Spined Loach (*Cobitis taenia*). This fish has a light brown body with lines of black blotches along the back and on each side. It has a two-pronged retractable spine below each eye.

Tropical Loaches live well in darkened aquaria with a muddy bottom layer containing some objects (such as pieces of broken earthenware vases etc.) under which the fish can hide. The Coolie Loach (*Acanthophthalmus kuhlii*), is found in Java and Sumatra,

and has a long eel-like body ringed by 15 to 20 dark brown or black bands. The nickname of Clown Loach is given to *Botia macracantha*, found in Sumatra and Borneo, which is one of the biggest Loaches, 30 cm long. It has brilliant colours; the body is either yellow or orange with three large black wedge-shaped bars, and its fins are red. It requires a temperature of 24 °C in aquaria.

Siluriformes. This name is applied to a large group of fishes more commonly known as Catfishes. There are many families of catfishes and this represents a major systematic group, in effect an order of fishes. In spite of the different characteristics amongst these families, it is possible to point out some peculiarities that are constant to them all. First of all, all Catfishes have from 2 to 5 pairs of barbels (some short, some long) around the mouth. The skin is not covered with scales of a normal kind, most are in fact scaleless, others are covered by a rough armour of bony plates (often spined). In many cases, the first rays of the pectoral and dorsal fins have a robust and sharp spine in the anterior part. An additional (often well-developed) adipose fin grows, in many species, between the dorsal fin and the tail fin. Catfishes have a swim-bladder and a set of weberian ossicles, which, as in the Carp family, are connected to the inner ear. There are about 2,000 known species of Catfishes the great majority of which live in fresh water in all continents, especially in tropical zones. The European Catfish or Wels (*Silurus glanis*) found in rivers of central and eastern Europe is a typical scaleless Catfish. It grows to huge proportions reaching 5 m and 400 kg in weight. Its elongated body is a dark shade of greenish-grey. The Black Bullhead (*Ictalurus melas*) can be considered a 'classic' type of Catfish. It has four pairs of barbels and a slate-grey body; exceptionally it can grow up to 50 cm and weigh 1·5 kg. It is native to the eastern and central regions of the United States, and was introduced into Europe in about 1880.

Other Catfish are much more valued for life in the aquaria — the strange-looking Glass Catfish (*Kryptopterus bicirrhis*), for instance. It is a small, light-yellow fish, measuring not more than 10 cm with a glass-like transparency so that its vertebral column is clearly visible. Amongst the African species, we will mention the *Synodontis schall* (Nile, Senegal, Lake Chad, etc.), a fish depicted on ancient Egyptian monuments. It is usually about 40 cm long, and has three pairs of barbels (the lower — or

Kryptopterus bicirrhis, an Indonesian Catfish, with characteristic long barbels and a transparent body.

71

Left: *Hemiancistrus vittatus*: the heavily armoured body gives this fish an appearance similar to that of some fossil fishes. Top right: One of the numerous species of *Corydoras*, all of which are native to South America. Bottom right: A small *Dermogenys pusillus*, which lives in south-east Asia.

mandibulae — pair of these are forked). The fish fauna of South America contains a great number of Catfish. The Argentine 'bagre amarillo' (*Pimelodus clarias*), widely distributed from Central America southwards, is an example of the non-armoured type. It measures about 30 cm in length; it has three pairs of barbels and is covered in large brown blotches. From this area come similar species and also the genera *Rhamdia* and *Pimelodella*.

All armoured Catfishes are indigenous to South America. One which is characteristic is also well-known to aquarists: the Spiny Catfish or Talking Catfish (*Acanthodoras spinosissimus*) from the Amazon. Its name is fully justified, as there is a line of needle-sharp spines running along each side of the body, as well as at the beginning of the dorsal and pectoral fins. It makes a characteristic sound by moving the pectoral fins, amplified by the swim-bladder. The many species of Corydoras — not many larger than a few centimetres — have only one pair of barbels, but are well protected by the two series of bony plates running along each side of the body. They prefer to inhabit slow-running water and are semi-amphibious in their behaviour. They do very well in aquaria at a temperature of 18° to 20°C, and perform a very useful role

as water cleaners by eating up debris that accumulates at the bottom of the water. One of the best known species is the *C. aeneus* distributed from Venezuela to Argentina: it grows to a maximum of 7 cm and is light brown with beautiful streaks of varying colours. The Catfishes belonging to the genera *Loricaria* and *Plecostomus* bear a startling resemblance to prehistoric fossilized fishes: the body is completely covered by series of plates set in rows; the mouth is set back on the lower part of the head and has broad lips enabling it to be used as a sucker. They feed mainly on algae.

Hemiramphidae. Only a few species of this family (the Halfbeaks) live in fresh waters; the rest are tropical marine fishes. They all have a very long body; the fins are not supported by spines; a short upper jaw and the lower jaw form a long, slender bill.

Dermogenys pusillus, which lives in Thailand and in the Sunda Islands — in fresh water as well as brackish — is pretty enough to be kept in the aquarium. It is 6 to 7 cm long; with males, which are smaller than females, bearing a distinctive red spot on the dorsal fin. This species is viviparous and has internal fertilization. Between 12 and 20 fry — 1 cm in length — are born after eight weeks. These fishes are good swimmers and like to live on

Two African species of
Toothcarps:
Top: *Aphyosemion*.
Below: *Nothobranchius*.

the surface of the water. A section of
the male's anal fin is modified into a
sexual organ. *Hemiramphodon po-
gonognathus* has a very similar geographical distribution, and behaves in
the same way as *Dermogenys*, although it has a longer lower jaw.

Cyprinodontiformes. Until very recently this name used also to include
a group of fishes of a different order
— now separately classified under
Atheriniformes. It is, however, a
well-defined group of two principal
families (Cyprinodontidae and Poeciliidae) both having rather obvious
characteristics in common. They are
all either small, or even tiny; they have
cycloid scales, fins lacking stiff spines;
no lateral line and a swim-bladder
which does not communicate with
the oesophagus. Sexual dimorphism
is very evident because the sex of
every individual produces differences
in size, colour and shape of fins.
Hybridization is common. These fishes
are found both in fresh and brackish
water all over the world.

The family Cyprinodontidae or Toothcarps owes its name to the fact that
its members resemble the cyprinids,
and they have teeth. Reproduction is
by laying eggs which are fertilized, as
in most fishes, after they are shed.
Aphanius fasciatus is widely distributed around the Mediterranean

coastline; the male fish has silver and
brown alternate stripes across its body.
The Blue Panchax (*Aplocheilus panchax*) is found in the south-eastern
regions of Asia and is rather varied in
its coloration: the male fish has a
characteristically coloured tail fin
(black on the outside and yellow or
orange on the inside). The very handsome species of genera *Aphyosemion*,
Epiplatys, *Nothobranchius* are native
to equatorial Africa. The members of
the genus *Aphyosemion* are adapted
to life in small ponds and puddles. In
the aquarium they need a dim light,
with rich vegetation and a temperature not over 24°C. Some species lay
their eggs on plants and others on the
bottom. The multicoloured and variable Nigerian species, Arnold's Lyre-
tail (*A. arnoldi*), measures up to 6 cm
in length; in the males the tail fin is
extended at the corners by two prolonged rays. It usually swims at the
surface, where it catches its small
prey. The Fire-mouth Epiplatys (*Epiplatys chaperi*) lives in West African
rivers: it has a series of brown vertical
stripes of varying length on its sides.
The American fauna also includes
many interesting Toothcarps. Various
species of *Fundulus* are found in lakes
and rivers of North and Central
America; the behaviour and ecological
preferences of each species varies

considerably and this must be taken into account when choosing them for the aquarium. The eggs are deposited on plants and hatch after 8 to 15 days. Relatively large (up to 15 cm in length) are the Striped Killifish (*F. majalis*) (from New Hampshire to Florida) and the Gulf Killifish (*F. grandis*) (Florida and Gulf of Mexico): both these fishes also live in salt water. The members of the genus *Rivulus* are numerous also, being widely distributed from the southern United States to Argentina, in running water rich in vegetation. The female fish (with a bright ringed black spot on its tail fin) has been responsible for the name *R. ocellatus.* The Argentine Pearlfish (*Cynolebias bellottii*) is only found in the basin of La Plata (Argentina). Its display of beautiful colours — as well as size and shape of the fins — differ according to sex. The male is a little larger — up to 7 cm — with an olive-green body and blue back; it has a dark vertical stripe that goes through the eye, and numerous pale blue flecks on its sides. The female is brownish olive with brown specks and vertical stripes. This fish is famous for its 'annual' life cycle — which can be completed in as little as eight months. *C. bellotti* inhabits ponds that can seasonally dry up. The adults will consequently die, while the eggs, which are deposited in the mud,

are kept moist until they hatch.

The members of the family Poeciliidae differ from those of the last described family mainly in their reproductive habits. Fertilization is internal and the male fish has a tube-shaped copulatory organ (the gonopodium) on the underside, which is, in fact, a modification of the first few rays of its anal fin, ending with little hooks. This, of course, makes the identification of sexes very easy in these fishes. They are all viviparous. The females which are larger than the males, are duller in colour, and have a characteristic black marking ventrally in front of the anal fin during pregnancy, which generally lasts 30 to 40 days. The number of fry at birth varies (but can run into tens) according not only to particular species, but also to the mother's age, and condition (availability of food etc.); they grow rapidly. All live-bearing Toothcarps are American and are plentiful in the tropics.

The Mosquito Fish or Spotted Gambusia (*Gambusia affinis*) is greenish or olive green, only growing to 4·5 cm (females). It is a North American species, but has been introduced to many parts of the world, to combat malaria; this has made it one of the best known members of the family. It adapts to all kinds of ecological conditions. The male fishes are less

One of the most beautiful varieties of Guppy, or Million fish (*Poecilia reticulata*). The beautiful coloration is characteristic of the male fish.

The Platy (*Xiphophorus maculatus*), originating from Mexico, is one of the species most widely kept by aquarists.

A Perch (*Perca fluviatilis*), one of the best known freshwater fishes living in Europe.

numerous than the females, and the latter give birth to anything between 2 or 3 to 100 fry at a time. The fry become adults in about fifty days. The Mosquito fishes imported into Italy (in 1922) belong to the sub-species *G. a. holbrooki*. The distribution of the One-spot Live-bearer (*Poecilia vivipara*) is very wide (from Venezuela to La Plata basin). This species is identified by the round black mark at each side and a black-edged dorsal fin: both these markings are more pronounced on males which grow to 4 cm. The names *Lebistes* and *Mollienisia* are now considered to be synonyms of *Poecilia*.

Poecilia reticulata (formerly *Lebistes r.*) is also known as 'Guppy' or 'Millions fish' (because it is so numerous). This minute and attractive fish is indigenous to South American waters (from Venezuela to north Brazil) but for years has been bred for small aquaria. It has very delicate and varied coloration: the male fish has a black spot on its sides at times, and only measures 3 cm, while the female grows twice as big. This species tolerates temperatures ranging from 15° to 24°C, and is very prolific; the newly born fry, however, are often devoured by the adult fish. Genetic studies carried out on them have revealed that some features are geneti-

cally dominant (e.g. normal-rounded tail fin), and that some are recessive (e.g. large 'flag-like' tail fin). Magnificent fishes are the Sailfin Mollies (*Poecilia* (=*Mollienisia*) *latipinna* and *P.* (=*Mollienisia*) *velifera*). The first lives in the coastal zones of the eastern United States to Yucatan; the second is restricted to Yucatan. Both species are relatively large (12 and 15 cm, respectively, when living in their natural environment, smaller if captive in aquaria). A most eye-catching characteristic of both species is the huge dorsal fin. They have similar colours, but different markings on the body and fins. Some individuals are wholly or partly black ('Black Mollies'); a similar melanism also occurs in *Gambusia*. These live-bearing Tooth-carps do well in large aquaria with many water plants and a temperature of 24° to 28°C. Amongst the best aquarium species must definitely be placed the Swordtails (*Xiphophorus helleri* and *X. maculatus* (=*Platy-poecilius m.*) originating from Mexico and Guatemala. The first of these two species is larger (male fish measure 8 cm and females 12 cm) and is identified by the prolonged lower half of the tail fin that extends into a 'sword' shape on the male fish. The colour can be green, red or golden. Change of sex with age is not rare

78

with these fishes. The Platy is only half the size of the Swordtail and has a stouter body. Its coloration can vary even more than in the preceding species (being red, golden, light blue, black, and may or may not have spots) and for this reason the *X. maculatus* makes an ideal subject for the study of heredity. The two *Xiphophorus* species cross very successfully.

Gasterosteidae. All the few species belonging to this family are called Sticklebacks, because of the row of sharp isolated spines along the back. They are small fishes living in fresh water, as well as brackish water and the sea. The best known is the common Three-spined Stickleback (*Gasterosteus aculeatus*) distributed widely throughout most of Europe, north and central Asia, and North America. Very occasionally the female fishes — normally bigger than the male — reach 12 cm. The Stickleback is a eury-thermic and strongly euryhaline fish. Occasionally found in the sea especially in the north, it is lively, pugnacious and carnivorous. Its mating habits are very characteristic and interesting and can be observed in the aquarium. The brilliant breeding coloration appears between April and July and is particularly notable in the male fish: green eye patches, red underside and beautiful rainbow-like mixture of

green, blue and silver along its back. The build-up of hormones during the breeding season gives the male a strong instinct to fight as well as to build a nest. It builds a roundish nest using chopped-up vegetation cemented with a gluey substance secreted from the kidneys. The nest itself is either built among the plants or placed on the bottom. The female fish, attracted by the male, enters the nest and lays between 100 and 400 eggs in it. Thereafter the male remains on duty keeping the nest strictly guarded until, after about 10 days, the larvae hatch.

Percidae. This family is the typical representative of one of the major groups of fishes, the percoids. They are mainly marine species, belonging to several families with several characteristics in common, such as having spiny rays in the fins, and the relative positions of the pelvic and pectoral fins, the latter placed on the thorax, while the swim-bladder is separated from the oesophagus. The Common Perch (*Perca fluviatilis*) is greenish with several dark vertical bands across the body, with reddish pelvic and anal fins. It can grow to 50 cm in length and weigh 3·5 kg. It inhabits the rivers and lakes of Europe, northern Asia, and North America. It is a voracious, carnivorous fish (which must be taken

A Pumpkinseed (*Lepomis gibbosus*), a fish originating from North America. is often found in Italian waters.

Chanda lala, a small Asian fish well known to aquarists.

into account in stocking the aquaria). The small Johnny Darter (*Etheostoma nigrum*) (6·5 cm) has a cloudy olive-coloured body with brown spots. It is a native of the United States where it is widely distributed: it prefers cold water; it lays eggs under the gravel and the male guards them until hatched.

Centrarchidae. All fishes belonging to this group belonged originally to North America, but several species have been introduced into other parts of the world. Its members have a marked resemblance to the percoids: it has similar spiny rays in the front of the dorsal and anal fins. Most species have a varied and multicoloured appearance. Naturally occurring hybrids between the species are often found in their natural environment. They are carnivorous fishes. Centrarcids thrive in large aquaria with a sandy bottom layer and having lots of plants and hiding places. Amongst the species established in Europe are the Pumpkin-seed Sunfish (*Lepomis gibbosus*) – very seldom growing beyond 15 cm in length and easily identified by the distinctive black spot with a red or orange edge on the gill cover tip; and the Largemouth Black Bass (*Micropterus salmoides*) is much larger – reaching a length of over 50 cm – and is less colourful than the last species. It prefers still or slow-running waters.

Centropomidae. This is a family of fishes (commonly called Glassfishes) living along tropical coastal regions – mainly in the Indo-Pacific region – and found in fresh water, in the sea and in brackish waters. Smaller species are popular fishes among aquarists, they have an almost transparent body of small size, not more than a few centimetres long, and are silver with delicate rainbow-like shiny tinges of colours. The dorsal fin is higher at the front end as also are the spines in the first dorsal fin; the anal fin is also elongate. The best known species are *Chanda lala*, *C. ranga* and a few more – all belonging to tropical Asia and Indonesia. *Gymnochanda filamentosa* (Malaysia) is one of the more popular; it has a characteristic scaleless body and the male is distinguished by the very elongate rays in both the dorsal and anal fins. It is advisable to use slightly salty aquarium water for these fishes.

Toxotidae. The name Archer fish is an appropriate description for a few species belonging to this family of spiny-finned fish. They are found in southern Asia, India, and China, as well as the Philippines and Australia. *Toxotes jaculator* is the best known. It grows to a maximum length of 24 cm; on the lower part of each side there are 4 to 6 broad black bands

Opposite page: The *Gymnochanda filamentosa* is a fish that lives in Malaysian fresh waters, easily recognizable by the characteristic shape of the fins.

80

separated by spots. This fish prefers brackish water, often among mangroves, and it keeps near the surface. Its mouth is structured in such a way that it can squirt out water to a distance of $1\frac{1}{2}$ m and catch insects flying past. The Archer fish thrives in aquaria provided that there is ample surface area and slightly salty water at a temperature of 26° to 28°C. *Toxotes jaculator* was first discovered in Java, and is present throughout Thailand and India to the Philippines. Ever since the 18th century, it has been famous for its characteristic 'archer's' skill; the need for a continuous supply of live insects for its diet may, at times, prevent this fish from being kept in aquaria.

Scatophagidae. This family lives either in the sea – along the coast – in brackish water or in fresh water. Its members are distributed in southern Asia and the islands of Asia. There are few species and they all have the same characteristic shape of body, which is compressed and high, with either stripes or spots of different colour. They are truly omnivorous; they even consume a vast quantity of mud. The most common species is *Scatophagus argus* which grows up to 30 cm long; greenish brown with numerous darker brown and black spots, arranged more or less in vertical series across the body. Like the Archer Fish, it needs a very large aquarium, with plenty of vegetation which will also form part of its diet; the water must contain a little salt for the smaller individuals, while larger ones prefer sea water. The Scats, as they are called, are euryhaline fishes.

Nandidae. This is a family with only few species spread across a vast area; they are found in north-eastern South America; West Africa, southern Asia and Indonesia. All the nandids are carnivorous and predatory: they need darkened aquariums, with plentiful vegetation. The Leaf fish (*Monocirrhus polyacanthus*) measures 8 cm and is found in Brazil and Guyana. It is an interesting fish not only for the oval and high shape of its body, pointed snout and protractile mouth, but also for the peculiarity of its behaviour. It is a slow swimmer and, with the aid of its coloration and markings, it mimics a fallen leaf, drifting on the water. However its inert position is deceiving because it soon snatches up and eats any unlucky fish that happens to come within its reach. It is necessary to cater for its constant need of live fish when keeping it in an aquarium.

Badis badis (8 cm) is common in still waters throughout India; this fish is popular with aquarists for its beautiful

Left: Archer fish (*Toxotes jaculator*) is a fish that owes its name to the ability to catch insects.
Right: A Scat (*Scatophagus argus*).

colours that vary frequently and quickly within the same individual, as well as between individual fishes.

Cichlidae. This is a large family composed almost entirely of freshwater species, mainly belonging to the tropics of the Old and New World. They are abundant in central and South America, and in Africa, where they are found in large numbers with a limited number of Asian species (Syria, Israel, India). The characteristics of the family are: the presence of one nostril on each side of the snout instead of two as in the majority of fishes; an interrupted lateral line; a rounded tail fin, and the presence of sharp spiny rays in varying numbers in the dorsal fin. They also have numerous small teeth set on a large and flat pharyngeal bone, and others of different shapes in the jaws. These fishes prefer still or slow-running water; they are herbivorous, omnivorous or carnivorous and often very specialized in their diet. The cichlids are interesting fishes from the point of view of their breeding habits: they exercise great parental care in various ways. Many species, for example, incubate the eggs by either keeping them in their mouths (either parent performs this duty) and even protects the newly hatched fry in the same way. The cichlids include many ornamental aquarium species and they are usually easy to rear.

The Scalare (or Angelfish) is undoubtedly the best known member of this family. Two names were given to this fish (*Pterophyllum scalare* and *P. eimekei*), however it seems very probable that they are only one species: both types have been widely kept in aquaria and cross-breed successfully, producing fertile hybrids. The appearance of this beautiful fish is unmistakable: apart from the ordinary coloured wild fish, which are silvery with vertical black stripes, there are some with completely black bodies. The two sexes are alike. They may attain a maximum of 15 cm length but the body depth can be up to 20 cm. The Angelfish thrives in aquaria with plenty of vegetation; the temperature must be kept close to 18°C. The eggs are laid on large leaves of plants and the fry are looked after by both parents. This cichlid originates from the Amazon regions.

Much more numerous are the species belonging to some American families, such as *Cichlasoma*, *Aequidens*, *Geophagus*, and *Apistogramma*. Unlike the Angelfish, these fishes have less well developed vertical fins and the profile of the head is rounded. The Chanchito or Chameleon Cichlid (*Cichlasoma facetum*) is very com-

Left: The Leaf fish (*Monocirrhus polyacanthus*) Right: A cichlid fish of the genus *Tilapia*, widely spread in Africa.

83

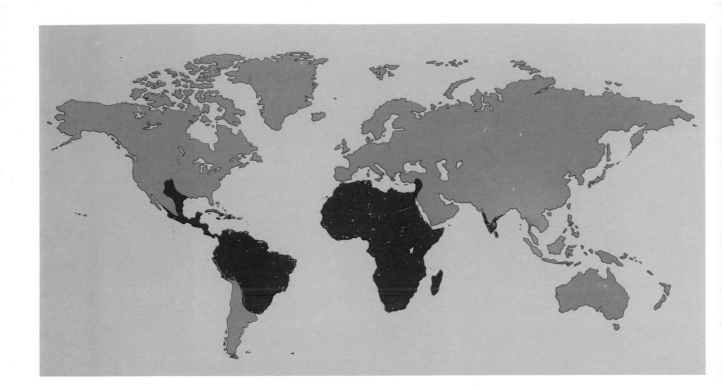

Above: A map showing the world-distribution of cichlids.
Centre: *Hemichromis bimaculatus*, a fish frequently kept as an aquarium specimen.
Below: *Pelmatochromis kribensis*, one of the most beautiful species of African cichlids.

Opposite page: Top: *Astronotus ocellatus*, an eye-catching South American cichlid.
Below left: *Pseudotropheus auratus*, an African fish.
Below right: *Cichlasoma severum*; Together with other related species, this fish belongs to South America.

Above: Scalare Angelfish
(*Pterophyllum* sp.) the
best known of the cichlids
originating from the Amazon.

Opposite page: Top left: A
Black Angelfish, a melanic
variation. Top right: *Uaru
amphiacanthoides*, a cichlid
originating from the Amazon.
Below: A species of
Symphysodon.

mon in Argentina, and was the very first cichlid bred in captivity (1884). It does not have a particularly showy appearance and grows to a maximum of 30 cm in length. It has some black vertical stripes on its body, but can, at times, be completely black, although the red eyes produce a startling contrast of colours. The smaller *Cichlasoma severum* (up to 20 cm) originates from Guyana and the Amazon. The coloration of this fish is very variable, as it can change with age and at any time. Several black vertical bars are present in the young fish but only the last persists once the fish matures. The overall shape of the body is also similar to that of many other species of cichlid, such as *Aequidens portalegrensis* (Brazil) which reaches 25 cm in length in its natural state. This fish, too, changes its coloration when reaching maturity: a longitudinal dark stripe is accompanied by two black spots, more or less distinct, one of which is on its caudal peduncle. This species is omnivorous and the eggs are deposited in a little hollow dug in the bottom. The Keyhole Cichlid (*Aequidens maroni*) owes its strange name to the elongated black spot seen on each side of its body.

The term Pompadour indicates the fishes of the genus *Symphysodon*, which is an American family with a

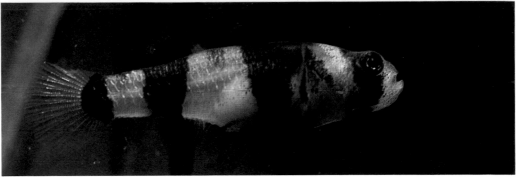

few species, all belonging to the Amazon basin. *S. discus* (20 cm) is the best known. This fish is very flat laterally and, as the name suggests, has a round shape. It becomes very colourful at spawning time, when some brilliant blue stripes can be seen across its sides. This fish is not easy to rear in aquaria. The quality of the water must be accurately controlled and the temperature kept between 26° and 30°C. The diet consists of small insects and crustaceans (*Daphnia*). *Apistogramma ramirezi* is considered to be a 'dwarf' cichlid, as it grows to no more than 5 cm in length. It originates from Venezuela. It is undoubtedly one of the prettiest and has vivid colours, but it, too, is delicate in aquaria.

The African cichlids are particularly interesting for their marked ecological and behavioural differences; they are found in great abundance in lakes and sometimes, as in Tanzania, for example, they comprise by far the largest majority of all fishes. The species of *Tilapia* are found also in south-west Asia, require large aquaria with plenty of vegetation, affording hiding-places. *Tilapia nilotica* grows to 50 cm in length; it has a black patch on each gill cover, and dark vertical stripes across its sides. *Hemichromis bimaculatus* is much more appreciated

by aquarists for its small size (not over 15 cm).

Gobiidae. This is one of the largest families of fishes. There are many species – all small or very small – living in fresh water, sea water, or brackish water all over the world in tropical and temperate zones. The pelvic fins are usually joined together, they have two dorsal fins, and an oblong or rounded tail fin. They are typical bottom-dwellers, often benthic in habit. While their appearance does not vary much, their mating habits are often characteristic of various species. They are carnivorous and often voracious. The identification of gobies, both of fresh water or marine type is never easy.

Some species of Gobies make attractive aquarium specimens. The best known is the Bumble-bee Goby (*Brachygobius nunus*) which measures 4 cm long. It has a yellow body with four contrasting dark brown vertical rings. This small fish is widely distributed from Thailand to the Sunda Islands. It lays its eggs under rocks. It needs slightly salt water and a temperature of 24° to 30°C.

There are a few species of Goby which differ from the rest, in that they have ventral fins which are not joined together. *Eleotris lebretonis* grows to a length of 12 cm. It is olive green with

Left: *Channa asiatica*, one of the best known fishes from southern China. Below: Top: The Three-Spot Gourami (*Trichogaster trichopterus*), a fish native to south-east Asia that is much valued by aquarists. Bottom: *Trichogaster microlepis*, this fish lives in the rivers of Thailand and Cambodia.

brown and red spots. It lives in West African rivers and attaches its eggs to plants. The small *Hypseleotris cyprinoides* (7 cm) has a translucent body with one dusky band along each side. The male fish is adorned with blue-edged fins. Its home is Indonesia.

Ophiocephalidae. This name means 'snake-head' and represents a family of fishes which are distributed both in Africa and Asia. They have flat heads, long bodies and cycloid scales. Their fins have no spiny rays; the dorsal and anal fins are rather long and the tail fin is round. Each gill chamber is extended into an upward branch, which has a network of blood vessels under the skin and which acts as an extra respiratory organ enabling the fish to survive for quite a while out of water. *Channa asiatica* is distinguished by the absence of the anal fin; it grows to a length of 30 cm. It is a greyish-brown, and covered in darker and lighter spots with a black round patch at the base of the tail fin.

Anabantidae. These are the Labyrinth fishes, so called because of a much folded and richly vascular auxiliary organ, known as the labyrinth, which is placed above each gill chamber. It is an extension of the gill arch, connected to the gill chamber and it consists of a series of lamellae covered with a membrane

full of enlarged blood vessels. These organs allow the fish to breathe atmospheric oxygen, taken in directly through the mouth, and the gas is absorbed into the blood as it flows through the capillaries. These fishes vary greatly in size according to species, and often have a very attractive coloration. The fins bear numerous stout spines.

Anabas testudineus was first discovered at the end of the 18th century and it is commonly known as the Climbing Perch. It grows to a maximum length of 25 cm; the body is a plain greenish grey in the mature fish and speckled in the juvenile; both have a dark stripe between the mouth and the eyes, one on the gill cover, and another at the base of the tail fin. The tail fin is roundish. The scales are ctenoid and closely set. This fish is extremely common all over Asia. The Climbing Perch is adaptable to variations in temperature, and also omnivorous. It can go from river to river, walking over dry land by using its stout fin spines in the pelvic fins. The Fighting-fishes, members of the genus *Betta*, are amongst the most sought after aquarium specimens. The best known species are *Betta splendens* (6 cm) and *B. punax* (9 cm). They have a short dorsal fin, while the anal and tail fins are spread out

into a fan shape. The coloration is extremely varied. These fishes build a characteristic 'bubble nest', air contained in mucus from the mouth. The nests are placed in amongst the plants and the eggs are laid in it by the hundred. The larvae hatch after on 24 to 30 hours. These fishes are carnivorous. They do well in aquaria, preferably in shallow water at a temperature of 25° to 28°C. They also like a good illumination and lots of vegetation. Fighting-fishes cannot be mixed with other fishes.

Many other anabantids also breed in aquaria and make 'bubble nests' similar to those of the Fighting-fishes. *Colisa fasciata* (12 cm) has a long dorsal fin and thread-like pelvic fins: it has a brownish-green body, with blue tinges and with red or orange stripes along the flanks. The members of the genus *Trichogaster* are very similar. *Trichogaster trichopterus* measures about 15 cm and is a silvery olive or bluish colour; *T. leeri* (11 cm) is easily identified because it is heavily speckled with white or yellow and has a thin black line across its side. The giant of this family is the Gourami (*Osphronemus goramy*) which reaches 60 cm in maximum length. It has a characteristically protruding jaw, filamentous pelvic fins, and a short dorsal fin set towards the tail

The Gourami (*Osphronemus olfax*); the coloration of this fish varies with age.

Opposite page: Top: *Calamoichthys calabaricus*, which resembles an eel with the body covered in thick scales. Below: *Tetraodon fluviatilis* a small species of Pufferfish suitable for aquaria.

end. Young individuals are reddish brown, while the mature fish is jet black.

Cottidae. The strong bone developed at the side of their heads is characteristic of these fishes, as it is of their numerous relatives found in the sea. The Sculpins are, in fact, mostly marine species widespread in the Arctic and cold seas. The group is represented in fresh water by a few species, such as the Bullhead (*Cottus gobio*). This fish is about 15 cm long; it has a large head, no scales and two dorsal fins. The back is brown on the upper parts with darker spots.

Tetraodontidae. They include the 'Pufferfish' or 'Globe fish'. Their name, Tetraodontidae, literally means 'four teeth'. The body is scaleless and smooth apart from a small patch (on the underside) where there are some tiny retractable spines. The Pufferfishes are mostly marine species living in warm waters, but there are a few fresh water species, as well. They are carnivorous. Some minute individuals can make good aquarium specimens. In normal conditions their body is the typical elongate fish-shape. They have large side sections of the stomach which they fill with water or air, so that the fish swells up until it becomes spherical. *Tetraodon lineatus* (40 cm) is found in many African regions: it has a slate-grey back with lines of the same shade going along the side. In India and the Philippine Islands one finds *T. fluviatilus* (17 cm) which is green with black patches on the back.

Polypteridae. These are the only members of a particular subclass of bony fishes, quite well defined by a series of characteristics, such as: thick shiny scales; stout isolated spines in a line along the back: the swim-bladder is ventral in position and divided into two uneven sections, it connects with the oesophagus and is used as an accessory respiratory organ. The body is elongated and the head is well protected by bony plates. In aquaria these fishes need adequate hiding places and a temperature of 22° to 28°C.

Polypterus bichir (70 cm) is found in the Nile, the Lake Chad and Lake Rudolf; it has a subspecies, *P. b. lapradei* found in West Africa. The Reed Fish (*Calamoichthys calabaricus*) is much longer (90 cm) but also much thinner and is found in the Niger delta and the Cameroons.

Dipnoi. This is another well-defined subclass, containing many different fossil species—mainly Palaeozoic— out of which only six are known to be still living. These fishes have a long body with the dorsal, anal and tail

fins continuous. They have mainly a cartilaginous skeleton. Their teeth are short and broad and form well adapted crushing plates. The main distinction, though, is in the respiratory and circulatory organs. The swim-bladder is rather large, is placed vertically and connected to the oesophagus, and forms, a lung (hence the common name Lungfish); the gills virtually cease to function when the fishes are out of water during their dry-season period of inactivity.

They are dividded into two families which comprise three genera. In the family Lepidosirenidae the scales are small, the pectoral and pelvic fins are filamentous, they undergo a form of metamorphosis during development, the lung is double. *Lepidosiren paradoxa* is found in South America; while the four species of Protopterus (*Protopterus aethiopicus* etc.) are distributed in Equatorial Africa. The second family is represented only by the *Neoceratodus forsteri* from the eastern regions of Australia. This fish has large scales, broad paired fins, a single lung; and does not undergo a metamorphosis. It is protected, because of its rarity. Because of its large proportions (above 1 m in length) it can only be kept in large public aquaria. Its diet is, of course, strictly carnivorous.

Marine Fishes

Selachii. Any list classifying fishes must begin with the selachians, as they have the most primitive characteristics. The skeleton is of particular interest; it is entirely cartilaginous, but, due to the hardening action of calcium salts, can become stiff enough to be mistaken for bone. The main overall distinction of cartilaginous — in contrast to bony — fishes is accompanied by many more characteristics, besides the structure of the skeleton, which are all equally important, but too lengthy to mention in this book. The cartilaginous fishes, or selachians — with a maximum of several hundred species — are essentially marine, and only in tropical regions are a few species found in fresh water. Their size ranges from medium to large, and for this reason they are not kept in aquaria very often, and (needless to say) certainly never in small domestic ones. In any case, one could not, by any stretch of the imagination, apply the word 'ornamental' to these fishes, for their coloration never compares with that of bony fishes.

Most interest centres on the sharks and the rays which have the largest number of species; while the only other group, the chimaeras, is represented by very few species, in the Mediterranean the only member being *Chimaera monstrosa*. The well-known term 'shark' requires some amplification. It is often considered to be synonymous with 'dogfish' whereas its meaning is much wider and embraces a very large number of fishes with the following characteristics: a fusiform body and a mouth set well back and ventrally beneath the head; a series of 5 (or occasionally 6 or 7) separate gill slits and associated gill chambers on each side of the head; the skin has a rough texture, as it is covered by tooth-like scales which give a very sharp-edged surface to it. The sharks, in common with all other selachians, have internal fertilization, and the males can be recognized by their external sexual organs, claspers which are attached to the inside of the pelvic fins. A large proportion of species are ovoviviparous, that is they give birth to young after a period of gestation during which the embryos are nourished by yolk from the eggs (but not with a placenta and thus without direct nourishment from the mother). There are, however, a few viviparous species (with embryos nourished through a kind of placenta) as well as egg-laying species.

Dogfishes are undoubtedly the most common species of sharks kept in aquaria, where they settle easily. Two species are very common in the Mediterranean. *Scyliorchinus canicula*,

Opposite page: A marine aquarium.

95

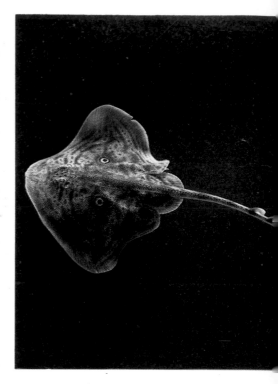

Top left: Greater Spotted
Dogfish (*Scyliorhinus
stellaris*), very common in
the seas of western Europe.
Bottom left: A Torpedo fish
(*Torpedo torpedo*).
Right: A Common Ray
(*Raja radula*).

commonly called the Lesser Spotted
Dogfish, is reddish, green or yellowish, thickly speckled in brown, It
grows to a maximum of 70 to 80 cm.
S. stellaris (Greater Spotted Dogfish)
which reaches a length of 1·5 m in
the Atlantic, is stouter and has larger,
but fewer spots. These fishes live close
to the sea-bed, in coastal waters, and
are active mainly at night. They feed
on smaller fishes and invertebrates.
They breed throughout the year and
lay eggs that are characteristic and
unmistakable: each egg is enclosed
within a brown horn case of rectangular shape, which has a twisted
tendril at each corner. These tendrils
help to attach the egg-case to objects
or to gorgonians on the sea-bed.
After a few months, the casing slits at
one end, and a fish 6 to 8 cm long
emerges.

The most common selachians in public aquaria are the Rays. The whole
order (Rajiformes) takes its name from
one of its groups, the rays (*Raja*).
These fishes are easily distinguished
from the sharks, in that they have a
dorso-ventrally compressed body,
with gills on the underside (instead
of on either side). Generally the tail
is long and very narrow, in contrast
with the broad 'disc' formed by the
head and body, and the vastly enlarged pectoral fins. Rays are ovi-

parous, as are the dogfishes, but the
corners of the egg-case have short and
slightly curved horns, and the case is
not attached, but left free at the bottom
of the sea. There are many species
(about fifteen are found in the Mediterranean) but they are not easy to
identify. The Thornback Ray (*Raja
clavata*) is the most common: it has
series of strong spines running along
the midline of the body, each embedded in a bony button; it measures
about 90 cm and is commonly found
in the Mediterranean and the eastern
Atlantic. The electric rays differ from
the true rays, in that their body has a
more rounded shape, their tails are
shorter and thicker, and they lack the
toothed scales. Furthermore they are
viviparous and have the famous
'electric organs', capable of inflicting
a considerable shock. These organs
which are used both defensively and
offensively, are evolved from special
muscles and are placed at each side
of the body. Common species in the
Mediterranean are *Torpedo torpedo*
recognizable by its occelate blue-
black spots, and the Marbled Electric
Ray (*T. marmorata*), with its warm
brown marbled colouring on a lighter
background. The stingrays—such as
Dasyatis pastinaca, from the European
coastal waters—are feared by fishermen, and rightly so. The very thin and

sharp spine in the tail (sometimes two spines are present) has venom glands at its base and the fish is therefore capable of inflicting severe injuries. Rays, electric rays and stingrays can all live in aquaria. They are all typical fishes of the sea-bed, and are well adapted to live on the bottom. They are all carnivorous.

Anguilliformes. The eels are a characteristic and well-defined order of fishes, forming a fall between the cartilaginous and the bony fish. The Common Eel (*Anguilla anguilla*) can be taken as typical. All the species have a very long, snake-like body, with a single fin running along the back and ventrally that is, in fact, a combination of dorsal, anal and tail fins. There are no pelvic fins or spines in the fins. The skin is smooth and scaleless, although the Common Eel, and some others, have rudimental scales. All eels are strictly marine — living at varying depths — apart from the several species of *Anguilla* which, like the Common Eel, have seasonal catadromous migrations. One of the most interesting characteristics is the metamorphosis through which they pass during development. The larva — still called a Leptocephalus, from the time when it was thought to be a distinct kind of fish — is completely different from the adult. It has a com-pressed, narrow, elongate body, rather resembling a leaf or a transparent ribbon, and gradually acquires its cylindrical shape and pigmentation.

The Moray Eels are one of the most important eel families and are identified by the absence of pectoral fins and tongue, as well as by the often bright coloration of the body. Numerous species live mainly in warm coastal zones. These fishes are carnivorous and voracious: they lurk hidden in amongst rocks, corals or sponges ready to snatch their prey. Some species are definitely aggressive even towards men. They do not have venomous glands as such, but their saliva contains toxic substances and for this reason their bite is dangerous. *Muraena helena* is the common Mediterranean Moray, and is also found along the southern coasts of Atlantic Europe. It grows to a maximum length of 1·3 m and is brownish black with yellow stripes and spots. It is a solitary inhabitant of the rocky sea-bottom; lives on fishes, molluscs, and crustaceans, and breeds in the summer. The Moray Eels of the genus, *Gymnothorax* possess many teeth that differ in shape and formation according to species. They are essentially tropical fishes, often with eye-catching coloration, which varies with age and species. *G. pictus*, which is covered

Left: The head of a common Mediterranean Moray Eel (*Muraena helena*).
Right: *Echidna nebulosa*, one of the colourful tropical Moray Eels.

in brown specks, found from the Red Sea to the central Pacific (Hawaiian Islands), *G. funebris* belongs to the Atlantic fish fauna; it is greenish in colour and very large (up to 1·8 m). *Echnidna nebulosa*, on the other hand, is a rather small (about 50 cm) but colourful Moray; some black patches, either star-shaped or ramified with a yellow or light brown centre, stand out on a light background. It has flattened molariform teeth, adapted so that it can crush shells. It is often found hiding amongst corals or rocks in the Red Sea, the Indian Ocean, and in the Pacific. *E. zebra* has the same geographical distribution and owes its name to the rather obvious alternate black-and-white stripes running across the body its whole length.

A fish which is often seen in public aquaria is the European Conger Eel (*Conger conger*). This is a very well known member of a family, which differs from the Moray in having both pectoral fins and a tongue. Its flexible body can often be seen moving gracefully amonst rocks. It is grey in colour and has a black edge all along its fin; it can attain a length of 2·4 m and weigh over 30 kg. The Conger Eel is carnivorous and is common throughout the Mediterranean and the eastern Atlantic. The metamorphosis of eels was first observed in this species.

Syngnathidae. No particular zoological knowledge is needed to recognize a Seahorse, with its atypical fish-shape. Other members of this family also share the rather tube-like mouth, which is usually small and toothless. Its whole body is covered by a protective series of bony plates; the gill opening is just a small hole. These rather quaint fishes are small and live mainly along the coastal zones of the sea but occasionally can be found further inland as they can adapt to brackish waters.

The genus *Hippocampus* contains the numerous species which are known as Seahorses, due to the angle at which their head is held (rather resembling the knight of a chess set). The body narrows abruptly behind the vent and ends in a long tail without a fin, which can wind itself around corals or algae. There are two European species: *H. guttulatus* and *H. hippocampus*. The first has a long snout and thread-like and often branched skin appendages on its body. Both have the same coloration, i.e. brown, slate grey, or olive green, and reach a length of about 15 cm. Some tropical species are larger, *H. kuda* for instance, which is found from the Red Sea to the Pacific Ocean. The Seahorse is famous for its reproductive habits. The eggs are put in a fleshy

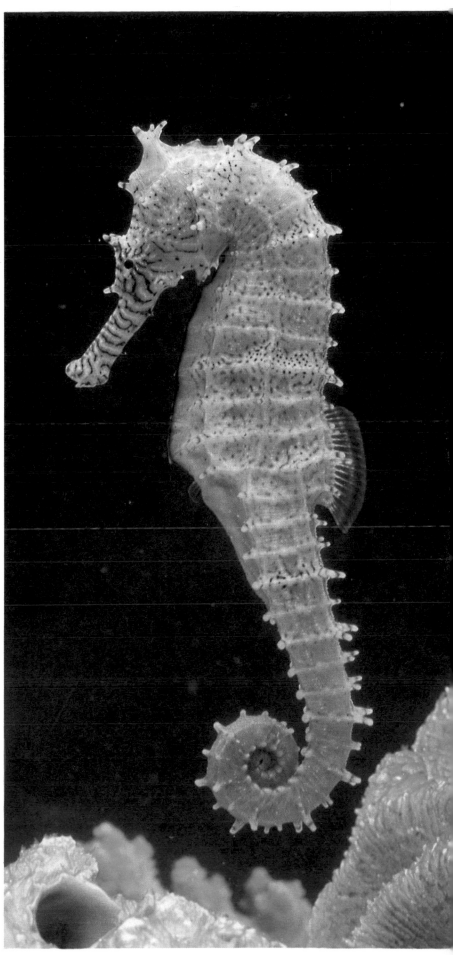

pouch on the underside of the male and remain there until they hatch and the fry are born; the incubation period seems to last about two months in the Mediterranean species. The newly hatched fish is a small replica of the adult. Seahorses do well in an aquarium at a temperature of about 20 °C. They swim rather slowly, holding their body vertically, with a rapid wavy motion of their dorsal fin. They are carnivorous and the best diet for them consists of small crustaceans.

The rest of the Mediterranean Syngnathidae are commonly called Pipefishes because of their long tubular shape. The head is not held at an angle but looks like an extension of the body. The Greater Pipefish (*Syngnathus acus*) grows to 35 cm in length, and has very variable colouring (grey, brown, reddish, olive green, etc., with either darker or lighter spots). It lives, as do the Seahorses, in shallow depths amongst fronds of algae and *Posidonia*. It has a straight tail which is not prehensile, and a tail fin. Once again the males incubate the eggs, in a long narrow fleshy flap (open in the mid-line) on their underside. Other species of this and different genera in the same family are commonly found in European waters. The name Pipefish is even more justified in the case of *Nerophis*, which have an almost

cylindrical body (as against a poly-
gonal cross-section in *Syngnathus*);
the tail is very thin and has no fin.
There are two Mediterranean species,
N. maculatus and *N. ophidion* (the
latter also occurs in the eastern
Atlantic), both growing to about
30 cm and living mainly amongst the
fronds of *Posidonia*. The coloration of
both can be very attractive. Seahorses
and Pipefishes are the best known
members of the family, but some
species with even more unusual
appearance live in other seas: the
Leafy Sea Dragon (*Phycodurus
eques*), for example, which resembles
a Seahorse, lives along the coast of
Australia.

Macroramphosidae. This long
name means simply, 'big snout'!
The snout of these fishes is, in fact,
extended into a thin tube ending with
a small toothless mouth. This is one
of the characteristics shared with the
members of the family Syngnathidae,
but there are others and all groups
form part of a larger order (Syngnathi-
formes). *Macroramphosus scolopax*
is commonly called the Trumpet fish
and has a very characteristic body: the
skin is rough on account of the finely
toothed scales. This fish is a silvery
pink and is only about 20 cm long.
It is common in the Mediterranean Sea
and is also found between 25 and

600 m in depth in all other ocean
waters. It does not take well to
aquarium life.

Holocentridae. These fishes (the
Squirrel fishes), are also easily identified. The overall shape of the body is
'normal', but they have very large eyes
and the free edges of the scales are
very spiny (strongly ctenoid); the fins
have very stout spines. More spines
can be found on the head and one is
forced to conclude that the Squirrel
fishes are . . . heavily armoured. The
colours red, orange, and purple are
prevalent and the surface is often very
shiny. These fishes are therefore eye-
catching specimens for an aquarium
where they do well, provided they have
sufficient hiding places. The Squirrel
fishes belong to the tropics and are
plentiful along coral reefs. Their diet
is always carnivorous. They belong
to the order Beryciformes amongst
which are a number of interesting
fossil species. The common name
Squirrel fishes indicates the genus
Holocentrus with a characteristic
strong spine placed on the angle of
the preoperculum. *H. ruber* is found
from the Red Sea to the Pacific Ocean
and has spread recently from the Red
Sea to the Mediterranean through the
Suez Canal: it is about 20 cm long.
H. ascensionis is larger (60 cm) and
lives in the Atlantic tropical waters

(the coasts of Africa and America). The two species are morphologically very similar. In both the body has longitudinal alternate red and white lines. Members of the genus *Myripristis* or Soldier fishes have fewer spines along the side. *M. murdjan* is found in the Indo-Pacific and *M. jacobus* in the tropical Atlantic: both these species are red and measure about 20 cm.

Mugilidae. We head the list of Perciformes with this family. The Perciformes has a large number of families amongst which we find many well-known fishes although they may look extremely different from one another. No less varied are their biological differences and their potential attractiveness to aquarists. This particular family of fishes, generally known as Grey Mullets, are found in all markets. They have a smoothly elongated body ending in a two-lobed tail fin, and two dorsal fins (the first of which consists of four spiny rays). The mouth is horizontally placed and has a series of tiny teeth. All species have alternate greyish-brown and silver stripes along the sides of the body. Grey Mullets are present in all tropical and temperate seas, they are extremely euryhaline and often swim up into brackish lakes. They are only kept in public aquaria because the mature fish grows to a

large size. The Striped Grey Mullet (*Mugil cephalus*) can grow to over a metre in length. It is identified by an adipose layer almost covering its eyes, like a thin veil. It is found all over the world and among all the species of its family it has the most food value. There are five more Grey Mullets in the Mediterranean, all of which are smaller, with normal eyes. Three of these (*Liza ramada*, *L. aurata* and *L. saliens*) have normal lips, while the other two (*Chelon labrosus* and *Oedalechilus labeo*) have a broad upper lip.

Apogonidae. A large group of small and colourful fishes, extremely popular with aquarists, can be admired in the coastal zones of all tropical waters. Many belong to the family Apogonidae and are usually found in such enormous numbers that they are an important ingredient in the food of larger fishes. Their general shape is similar to that of a common member of the Mediterranean fish fauna, *Apogon imberbis*. This fish, about 10 cm long, or a little more, has large eyes, a big mouth, two dorsal fins and a two-lobed tail fin. A vivid red (a frequent colour amongst apogonids) makes it stand out in underwater caves where it likes to live and where often it is caught by the underwater camera. *A. imberbis* is a typical coastal fish.

Left: *Myripristis murdjan*, a fish common in the Red Sea. Right: One of the various species of Mediterranean Grey Mullets.

101

As well as occurring in the Mediterranean *A. imberbis* is also found along the shores of the eastern Atlantic. Here, too, are found other species of the same family, such as *A. binotatus* (Bermuda, Florida, Bahamas, the Antilles), which has an obvious double black line across its back contrasting with the red of the body. These fishes are even more numerous in the Red Sea and in the Indian and Pacific Oceans. Among the attractive species that do well in the aquarium and are very ornamental should be mentioned, *A. brachygrammus*, which is all black, and the beautiful *A. nematopterus* with its unusually large fins and the broad black band crossing the anterior body on each side. *A. nigripinnis* is distinguished by a round black spot with a light edge on each side near the head, and a blunt (instead of two-lobed) tail fin. Some species of Apogonidae are interesting for their habits of associating with other organisms. *Astrapogon stellatus* (tropical western Atalantic), which is 7 to 8 cm long and brown and black in colour, lives in the mantle cavity of *Strombus gigas*, a large and well-known mollusc with a thick pinkish-white shell. The little fish only abandons the secure shelter offered by its host at night to search for the small crustaceans on which it feeds.

Left: A young individual of a red species of Grouper (*Mycteroperca rubra*); the juvenile coloration will change when the fish matures.
Below: *Epinephelus guaza*; this fish lives in the Mediterranean Sea and the Atlantic Ocean, and is one of the best known species of Grouper.

Paramia quinquelineata is only a few centimetres long and has black longitudinal lines on its back. It normally hides in amongst the spines of the Hat-pin Sea Urchin, well camouflaged by its stripes, on coral reefs in the Indo-Pacific.

Serranidae and related families. This group of fishes (Sea Perches) derives its family name from the Latin word *serra* (a 'saw'): the edge of the preoperculum has more or less well developed teeth. This characteristic is shared by other families or rather by a number of fishes which are difficult to identify and are therefore still not properly classified. However, the Sea Perches have strong jaws with good sharp teeth, rather small and usually ctenoid scales, and fins with several strong spines. The dorsal fin is generally long and forms a single fin; the pelvic fins are placed on the thorax (i.e. below the pectoral fins). These details deserve attention, as they are significant in placing the Serranidae close to another group of fishes whose family name Percidae is explained by a basic affinity with the Perches. They occur only in fresh water whereas the Serranidae are almost entirely marine fishes and are particularly numerous in warm coastal zones. In Europe the largest number of species are in the Mediterranean Sea.

All these fishes are predators and carnivorous. They can grow very large and are attractive with multicoloured spots and markings.

The Bass (*Dicentrarchus labrax*), is one of the best aquarium species. This handsome fish, with bright silvery sides (which in the fry are speckled with brown-black spots) can grow to over 1 m in length and weigh more than 12 kg. It prefers brackish water and is strongly euryhaline, often being found upstream at considerable distances from the sea. Its high food value is shared by many species of Serranidae from other parts of the world. The Striped Bass (*Roccus saxatilis*) is the American counterpart of the European Bass, and it is also sought after by fishermen. It is larger than the European species and easily distinguishable due to the slate-grey stripes running along its silvery sides. This fish goes to the river at spawning time.

The series of species of the serranids with the single dorsal fin, which are much more numerous, can begin with the Stone Bass (*Polyprion americanum*), which has a large head covered with strong bony ridges, which often have short spines on them. This fish, growing to a length of over 2 m, is a plain brown when mature, while the young have lighter

Opposite page: Top left: *Cephalopholis miniatus*, common in the Indian Ocean and the Red Sea; Top right: A species of *Epinephelus*. Centre: *Serranus scriba*, a species that, together with the one illustrated below is one of the most commonly found in the Mediterranean. Bottom left: *Serranus hepatus*.

This page: Left: *Cromipeltes altivelis*: the distinctive shape and coloration make this fish easily recognizable. Below: Another species of *Epinephelus*. To this genus belong many species which are widespread in tropical coastal zones.

blotches and lines. Only the latter can be kept in aquaria, as the mature fish would soon attack and devour smaller fishes. Typical among the serranids are those fishes that belong to the genus *Epinephelus*, and, some others, all known as Groupers. These are large fishes which lead a solitary life among rocks on the sea-bed or in coral reefs where they lie in wait for prey such as smaller fish or invertebrates. Coloration changes considerably with age, being much brighter in the young fish, which have spots, stripes and a variety of patterns, and almost uniform in the adults. Young Groupers are therefore greatly valued as ornamental fishes, and these fish are among the most attractive species in large aquaria. (Unfortunately they are often hunted by underwater divers.) Recent research has shown that they undergo a sex change with a longer female phase. Many of the Mediterranean serranids belong to the genus *Epinephelus* which has an enormous number of species. The Dusky Perch (*E. guaza*) is a brown fish (with lighter speckles when young) which can weigh over 60 kg. It is found throughout the Mediterranean, and its distribution also extends to the Atlantic where it occurs in the coastal zones of Africa, and, it is said, South America. *E. alexandrinus* is slightly

smaller and its coloration varies considerably with age. The young fish is brown with darker stripes along the body, which give way to a large gold patch when maturity is reached. Unlike these last two species, *E. aeneus*, which is of a greenish colour with two light stripes across its head, likes sandy bottoms. The so-called Nassau Grouper (*E. striatus*) can grow to be over a metre in length and is normally whitish grey with spots and vertical stripes either brown or black, its coloration, however, can vary, according to environmental conditions, so that in a few seconds it can change beyond recognition. *E. merra* and *E. tauvina*, together with many other species, are common from the Red Sea to the Pacific Ocean. The first can be identified by the many brown spots all over its body and fins, and a network of light white lines in between. The second fish is of a plain brown colour when fully grown, having lost the darker spots and stripes that are displayed when it is young. It grows to a maximum length of 2 m. There are species that grow to even larger size. One of these gigantic serranids, *E. lanceolatus* (found along the coasts of the Indian and Pacific Oceans) can grow to more than 3 m! Once again the juvenile is boldly marked, but the body of the mature

An elegant example of *Calloplesiops altivelis,* from Indo-Pacific seas.

fish is blackish all over. The members of the genus *Cephalopholis* — all of them tropical — are distinguished by the fact that they have fewer spines in the dorsal fin. There are three similar species — either red, orange or light brown — heavily speckled with blue dots. They are the *C. fulvus* (western tropical Atlantic), *C. miniatus*, and *C. argus* (Indo-Pacific).

The species *Mycteroperca*, which are mostly American, have more spines in the anal fin and characteristic peculiarities of the skull. One (*M. rubra*) is found in the warmer parts of the Mediterranean and in the Atlantic (including the American coast); it is 80 cm long and reddish brown in colour.

M. venenosa, only slightly larger than the last species, lives exclusively in the western tropical Atlantic, and has quite different colours: the body is covered all over with brownish-black patches and red spots. The name of this handsome fish indicates that its flesh can occasionally be poisonous. One of the most exotic species of serranid is *Cromileptes altivelis* (Indian and Pacific Oceans). It has a characteristic profile, as the head is much lower than the body; the young fish has fewer but larger and rounder black patches. This is one of the fishes which do not grow as large in captivity as they do when free. They only reach a length of 30 cm in an aquarium, while in their natural environment they can grow much larger. The same applies to *Hypoplectrus puella* (western tropical Atlantic), which has a relatively deep and short body, lightish in colour, with a few vertical darker stripes and blue bands across the head.

The Sea Perches, of the genus *Serranus*, are also well known, even though fishermen regard them as poor sport. They are smaller in size and therefore are more suitable for aquaria than the last group. They are carnivorous predators and live within coastal waters. For a long time they have been known to be hermaphrodites. *S. scriba* is undoubtedly one of the most colourful of Mediterranean fishes and can be easily recognized by its bright blue underside, broad vertical stripes in a brownish-black shade and, above all, by the network of blue lines on the reddish background of the head. It is about 20 cm in length and lives amongst rocks and beds of *Posidonia* growths. *S. cabrilla* is very similar in size and in ecological features but differs in coloration. It has vertical light brown stripes along the side with thin orange or yellow stripes across. *S. hepatus* is considerably smaller and has a black spot on the dorsal fin. This fish prefers deeper

Grammistes sexlineatus (adult).

water, as a rule, and can be found on fine sand or amongst the debris at the bottom of the water. The American serranid, *S. tigrinus* — known in the isles of Bermuda, Bahamas, the Antilles, and in Florida — is very colourful: it has black patches all over the greenish back and the bright yellow underside.

Centropristes striatus is common on the eastern coast of the United States where it is fished. It is brown or slate-grey and can grow to 60 cm in length. The particular phenomenon of sexuality (i.e. sex changes) in serranids is also evident in this species.

Decidedly ornamental are the red, orange or pink serranids of the genus *Anthias. A. anthias* is common in the Mediterranean, but is also found along the West African coast: it grows to a maximum of 15 cm. The pelvic fins are very large and the tail fin strongly forked. The body is red, with some yellow horizontal lines on the head. It is usually found in cave waters living in small groups and is only active at night. It is easy to keep in the aquarium. Its relation, *A. squamipinnis* — found from the Red Sea to the Philippines — has a very characteristic blue line that goes downwards from its eye to the base of the pectoral fin. *Callanthias ruber* is equally pretty: it grows to a length of 25 cm and is vividly coloured with a reddish-purple body and yellow fins; the tail fin is moon-shape and has two long streamers at the end. This fish lives in Mediterranean waters and the tropical eastern zones of the Atlantic. Its position amongst the serranids is not entirely established yet.

Grammistes sexlineatus (which is given its own family: Grammistidae) is easily recognized by the whitish-yellow lines along the sides: in the young fish the lines have regular interruptions along their course. They have rather smooth skin and grow to a length of 20 cm or more. It is a fairly common species of the Indian and Pacific Oceans. The *Gramma loreto* (family Grammidae) is one of the prettiest marine aquarium species. It only grows to 10 cm long and displays a beautiful coloration. The front part of the body is purple-red, while the other half is a vivid yellow, with a black patch on the front of the dorsal fin. It has an interrupted lateral line. *G. loreto* is found in the Atlantic Ocean (from Caribbean waters to Bermuda); it lives either in caves or in dark recesses under rocks, where it lies upside down. In the aquarium it can be rather aggressive towards its own species. *Pseudochromis paccagnellai* (family Pseudochromidae) has remarkable similarities to the species

A school of *Lutjanus kasmira*, a species that is common to the Red Sea and Indian Ocean.

described above, as it has the same colours and size (a few centimetres). It can, however, be distinguished by the fact that the spiny dorsal fin rays are much fewer and it has no black mark on its dorsal fin. This fish was only discovered very recently. It lives in Australian and Indonesian waters, and belongs to the large world of fishes inhabiting the coral reefs. Some sort of hiding place should be provided for it in aquaria.

Lutjanidae. For convenience sake many Perch-like fishes can be grouped together under this name, even though their classification into different families is rather more complicated. This is in fact a very mixed group of fishes, varying greatly both in form and structure as well as biologically. They live on tropical coastlines, often among coral reefs, and in other environments (mangrove swamps, for example); they are carnivorous or omnivorous, often gregarious. Many species have remarkable and attractive colours, which can change with age (they are more vivid in juvenile fishes). The difference in coloration between young and mature specimens is so vast that the same fishes could well be thought to belong to different species, when in different stages of development. Many species also grow to considerable size when fully mat-

ure; it is understandable why we only see young fishes kept in aquaria.

The lutjanids (Snappers) resemble the Sea Perches in that they have a characteristically serrate preoperculum and a similar robust dentition (some teeth are large and caniform) as befits carnivorous animals. Many species are found in the warm zones of all oceans. Very common from the Red Sea to Oceania is *Lutjanus kasmira* which is 30 cm long. It has a characteristic colour pattern that varies according to the individual; some light blue lines (often edged with black) run along its side and there is a blackish mark on the tail end. *L. sebae*, at least in its juvenile stage, is also very colourful; three large transverse bands of a reddish-brown colour make a contrast with the light pinkish colour of the body, but they fade as the fish matures. The first stripe cuts across the eye, to the end of the snout. This species has a deeper body than the last one, but its maximum size is more or less the same. *L. apodus*, however, is much larger (about 50 cm long) and has some light coloured vertical stripes across the side of the reddish-grey body (more markedly in the young fish). This species is found between the United States and Brazil and is very common.

Another group of species have weaker

112

teeth and a smooth preoperculum. The several species of *Gaterin* (the name is of Arab origin) are attractive enough to be kept in an aquarium, though not always easy to maintain; often they have great differences in colours, according to age. The outline of the head is convex in some species (while it is oblique in the Lutjanidae) and the lips are thicker. The distribution of the genus is limited to the Indo-Pacific Oceans. *G. gaterinus* is common in the Red Sea and the eastern Indian Ocean. It measures up to 40 cm; it has yellow fins with black dots and stripes. There are a few black lines going along the side of the body for a length of about 12 cm, which are well marked in the young and gradually fade away into dark speckled patches, as the fish matures. The young of the *G. chaetodonoides* (common in the Pacific but rather scarce in the eastern Indian Ocean) have a dark brown body with light roundish patches. *Haemulon flavolineatum*, about 30 cm long, has several wavy yellow lines running along the body: the inside of the mouth is red. In common with other related species, these fishes, found in great number around the southern parts of Florida and in the Caribbean, live in dense schools. *Anisotremus virginicus* – also gregarious and living

exclusively in the tropical eastern Atlantic – has a different outline, in that it has a higher back. It has horizontal yellow lines along the side and some contrasting black bands, of which one sweeps vertically across the body at the back of the head, and one goes on the slant from the back of the head to the snout.

Sparidae. These fishes (the Sea Breams), like the serranids are also typically Perch-like fishes, but all of them have a smooth preoperculum and have teeth only on the jaws (and not on the palate). The teeth have different formation according to the diet of the particular fish: in some species they may be sharp and caniform; in others flat but with cutting edges; or broad and rounded like molars, adapted to crushing hard food. For this reason tooth formation is a useful characteristic for the identification of individual Sea Breams. There are, in fact, quite a number of them, distributed in tropical and temperate seas; South African waters seem particularly suitable. Most Sea Breams live in coastal waters, but can go down to considerable depths, reaching a few hundred metres. The family has no members reaching the gigantic proportions of some Serranidae, but they can be on the large side nevertheless.

Left: This young *Gaterin chaetodonoides* seems almost poised on coral branches.
Right: *Lutjanus sebae* with its distinctive colour pattern.

113

The Sea Breams are well represented in the Mediterranean. The Dentrix (*Dentex dentex*) grows to over a metre in length, and has sharp dog-like teeth; it is in fact a predator and devours fishes and many cephalopods. It normally lives on rocky bottoms, but moves towards the shores in the summer. It differs from the Gilt-head Bream (*Sparus aurata*) – which is silvery grey all over, with golden patches around and between the eyes – in that it has a silvery, rosy or bluish tint on the body, often covered with black dots. The Gilt-head Bream is fairly large too (70 cm). It is euryhaline and seems quite at home in brackish water. Both the Dentrix and the Gilt-head Bream are considered good-quality food and are commonly fished in the Mediterranean. Various other fishes are also valued as food amongst this group; for instance, the members of the genus *Diplodus*, which are plentiful along the Italian coasts. They are similar to the Gilt-head Bream, with the same thick and molar-shaped teeth in the sides of the jaw, set in one or more rows. The species *D. sargus* has an oval-shaped silvery-grey body with a row of black vertical stripes along its sides. As in all members of this genus it has a large black patch at the base of the tail fin. This fish normally measures in the region of 20 to 30 cm, but it can grow to greater lengths. Similar to it, and equally common, is the *D. puntazzo* distinguished by its more pointed snout. *D. annularis* is much smaller, measuring up to 15 cm, and has a plain golden yellow body but has no dark stripes.

Lythognathus mormyrus is more elongated, with a silvery-grey body crossed vertically by a series of black or slate-grey stripes; it only reaches 30 cm in length. It generally lives on sandy bottoms and eats small invertebrates. One of the most easily identified Sea Breams is the Saupe (*Salpa sarpa*), a pretty fish with attractive yellow lines along its body, which lives in shoals amongst the rich vegetation of rocky bottoms. This species is herbivorous and in an aquarium lives on algae. *Oblada malanura* is smaller (20 to 30 cm), silvery grey with a contrasting black ring, running around the base of the tail. The Black Sea Bream (*Spondyliosoma cantharus*) grows to a larger size (50 cm): it is grey-brown with golden lines along the body, more or less marked. All these fishes (which are amongst the most commonly known in the Mediterranean basin) also live in the eastern parts of the Atlantic, some as far north as the British Isles. In the tropical western Atlantic (from the Antilles to Brazil)

114

lives *Calamus pennatula*, similar to the Gilt-head Bream in looks: the silvery grey of the body is heightened by delicate rainbow-like tinges and enhanced by blue and yellow lines on the sides of the head. *Mylio bifasciatus* is found in the Red Sea and Indian Ocean.

Mullidae. Two barbels under the lower jaw, used as tactile sensory organs, form the main characteristic of this group of fishes, the Red Mullets. There are two dorsal fins and the first one is equipped with slender, flexible spines: the tail fin has two lobes. The Red Mullets are colourful fishes, with plenty of red, pink, orange and yellow tints; their size is always fairly modest. They are all marine — mainly tropical — and feed on the bottom on small invertebrates. The best known are the members of the genus *Mullus*, of which two species live in the Mediterranean: *Mullus barbatus* (the Plain Red Mullet) and *M. surmulethus* (the Common Red Mullet). This last species is larger (40 cm) than the previous one and is more colourful, having yellow stripes along its side.

Their relatives, the Goatfishes (*Upeneus*) are strictly tropical, as is the Indo-Pacific *U. asymmetricus*: this has a wide yellow stripe along its side, which is typical of this family. *Paru-*

peneus barberinus is quite large (50 cm): it is commonly found from the Red Sea to the Hawaiian Islands and has a black line along its side with a black mark on the caudal peduncle.
Sciaenidae. These Perch-like fishes, usually known as Drums or Croakers, have two dorsal fins of which the first is very short and usually continuous at the base with the second; the tail fin is not forked. Sciaenids are marine, but many species live in brackish waters and some even in fresh water.

The *Umbrina cirrosa* is a well-known fish; it reaches a metre in length; it has a mass of wavy golden-yellow lines obliquely crossing the body, making a contrast with the silvery-grey background. This sciaenid is found near sandy shores or in river mouths. It feeds on crustaceans and other invertebrates. Its flesh is valued as an excellent food.

The Corb (*Sciaena umbra*) is normally no longer than 35 cm. It gets its common name of 'Crowfish' in Italian — *Pesce corvo* — from the darkish brown colour of the body of the front margins of the pelvic and anal fins. It makes its home on rocky sea-beds. It is found only in the eastern Atlantic Ocean and Mediterranean. *Equetus acuminatus*, which is smaller (20 cm), is also more ornamental: it has brown

The Corb (*Sciaena umbra*) is one of the most common Mediterranean fishes.

115

Left: The genus *Caranx* contains many species which are difficult to distinguish.
Right: *Gnathanodon speciosus* (juvenile).

Opposite page: A series of multicoloured Butterfly fishes.
Top left: *Chaetodon collaris.*
Centre left: *Gonochaetodon larvatus.*
Bottom left: *Chaetodon chrysurus.*
Top right: *Chaetodon plebejus.*
Centre right: *Chaetodon ephippium.*
Bottom right: *Chaetodon semilarvatus.*

stripes of varying thickness running horizontally along the whitish sides: the front part of the dorsal fin is much higher than the rest. It is an American species which is rather too delicate to keep in an aquarium.

Carangidae. The Jacks live a little further away from the coast than the fishes described so far, and often go in large schools; some species, however, are found in coastal zones. Generally the body is fusiform and rather elongated, but it can, at times, be laterally compressed and high; it is covered by minute scales, with two dorsal fins and a forked tail fin. A common and typical coloration – with greenish-blue back and silvery sides – is found in many species. Carangids are carnivorous and, in turn, their flesh provides excellent food. They must, however, be excluded from the list of aquarium specimens, for several reasons: they can grow to an unmanageable size; they need a great deal of space and food and are unable to adapt to life in an aquarium.

Caranx hippos is cosmopolitan in all warm seas and, in common with the numerous related species, has a series of small bony plates (scutes) along the second half of the lateral line. The related *Gnathanodon speciosus* is widespread in the Red Sea and the Pacific. It is distinguished by its

toothless mouth and the golden-yellow coloration with vertical dark lines (varying in thickness and intensity) running across its side. This fish can grow to a metre in length. Young specimens, which have even brighter coloration, are sometimes kept in marine aquaria. The Yellowtail (*Seriola dumerili*) has no bony scutes along the lateral line and has a golden-yellow band (more or less marked) along its side: it measures up to 70 cm. This fish is found in all ocean waters, as well as in the Mediterranean basin. The silvery-grey *Selene vomer* (tropical zones of the Atlantic) is about 30 cm long and is very characteristic of the carangids with very deep, laterally compressed bodies. Of the same type is *Scyris ciliaris* from the Indian and Pacific Oceans.

Chaetodontidae. The name of this family, the Butterfly fishes, means 'bristle tooth'. They are, without doubt, the most admired of all aquarium specimens for the beauty and splendour of their colours and forms, that can easily compete with those of exotic birds or rare butterflies. They have a small mouth with small slender teeth in each jaw. The body is high and laterally flattened with scales extending and covering parts of the dorsal and anal fins as well which makes these fins appear to be rather

high but part of the body, as a rule the tail fin forms only a single lobe. Coloration, as we have already mentioned, can be of outstanding variety and beauty.

The Butterfly fishes are found exclusively in tropical seas. They dwell mainly amongst coral growths and, in fact, form a characteristic part of the fauna of coral reefs. It follows that that they are found in particularly large numbers in the Indo-Pacific seas. They have sedentary habits and often take shelter in the cracks of rocks or among coral. Some species are solitary, others live in small groups. The great popularity of these fishes with aquarists is understandable, even though they are not easy to keep in captivity. Some care must be taken with their diet and the temperature of the water in the aquarium; and they must not be put with polyps or invertebrates, which they devour.

There are two quite distinct groups of Chaetodontidae, which should perhaps be considered as two separate sub-families. In some generas (*Pomacanthus* and its allies) stout spines point backwards on each side of the head, from the lower angle of the preoperculum. These fishes are usually known as Angelfish. The members of the other genera (*Chaetodon* and its relatives) lack the heavy spine on the

preoperculum and are smaller in size. All species are generally known as Butterfly fishes. They occur in great numbers and several are suitable for tropical aquaria. The shape of the body is generally the same, and differentiation is given mainly by coloration, and can be described best by the illustrations provided in this book, rather than by any verbal description. Length varies between 10 and 25 cm. Butterfly fishes roam amongst the coral out of which they eat the living polyps, and their presence lends a touch of mystery to the beautiful underworld of tropical waters.

Amongst the Red Sea Butterfly fishes we find *Chaetodon auriga*, with a short thread-like extension to the dorsal fin in adult fishes; *C. chrysurus*, with a contrasting brick-red colour covering the rear half of the body; and *C. semi-larvatus*, easily identified by the attractive yellow colour of the body broken only by a black patch on each side of the head. Other species from the Indo-Pacific are *C. ephippium*, with a wide black patch on the back; *C. meyeri*, with characteristic slanted black stripes contrasting with the blue on the sides; and *C. lunula*, endowed with a white patch on the top and one at the back of the head. Among representatives of this family found in the western Atlantic are *C.*

capistratus, which has a round black spot with a white halo, and *C. striatus*, with a few wide black bands standing out from a whitish background. The *Gonochaetodon larvatus*, which is very common in the Red Sea, is easily distinguished by the several white lines along the side, slanting at an angle. In the same sea *Heniochus acuminatus* is found; it is a gregarious fish, almost 20 cm long, that does well in aquaria. It has alternate black and white stripes along the side and the dorsal spines are greatly elongated and white in colour. Although they are rather difficult to maintain in captivity, two small and beautiful species must be mentioned; they are *Chelmon rostratus* and *Forcipiger longirostris*, both found in the Indo-Pacific. Both have very long snouts and they share another common characteristic in that they are aggressive towards individuals of the same species. *Forcipiger longirostris* differs from the other in that it is of a bright yellow colour and the snout is extended into an elongated tube.

Angelfishes rival Butterfly fishes in the beauty of their colouring which, however, can change substantially with age, the colours of the young fish being totally different from that of the adult. The change takes place when the fish reach 8 to 10 cm in length.

Left: *Pomacanthus semicirculatus* (juvenile); the adult of this species is a different colour. Right: *Pomacanthus annularis* lives in the Indian Ocean, as does the previous fish.

Opposite page: Top left: *Heniochus acuminatus* commonly seen along the coasts of the Red Sea. Top right: *Chelmon rostratus*; this fish displays a beauty of coloration that is common in all Chaetodontidae. Below: *Forcipiger longirostris*.

119

Right: *Pomacanthus maculosus* in its juvenile stage.
Below: The magnificent Emperor Angelfish (*Pomacanthus imperator*), one of the most beautiful fishes of the coral reefs. The characteristic spine at the rear of the gill cover is easily visible.

Top left: *Apolemichthys trimaculatus* from the Indian Ocean.
Right: A mature specimen of *Pomacanthus maculosus*, a species belonging to the Indo-Pacific.
Bottom: *Euxiphipops navarchus*. This fish displays bright contrasting colours, as do most Butterfly fishes.

Top left: *Chaetodontoplus mesoleucus*.
Right: *Centropyge flavissimus*.
Below: *Pygoplites diacanthus*, showing the characteristic striped pattern.

When kept in aquaria, they need adequate hiding places and the diet must include vegetable substances; the presence of more than one individual of the species must be avoided in the same tank. *Pomacanthus imperator* is one of the most eye-catching members of this group of fishes. It measure 40 cm; the body is blue with yellow lines along the side of the mature fish while the juvenile has white stripes arranged in a more or less regular semicircular pattern. *P. paru*, of the tropical Atlantic Ocean, is black with scales edged with yellow when fully grown; the young fish of this species are black with yellow vertical bands, very similar to the juvenile of *P. arcuatus*, which occurs in the same seas and, when mature, is grey with black spots. The species of *Holacanthus* differ from those already described in such details as the spines on the head and the scales. *H. tricolor* is common in the Caribbean and neighbouring waters; it is yellow in the front half of the body and tail fin and black elsewhere. *H. ciliaris*, also from the Caribbean, is green with some bright blue stripes and spots on the head. *H. asfur*, common in the Red Sea, and 15 cm long—is a blue-grey in colour with a broad yellow vertical band on each side; both the dorsal and anal fins are extended into a thin point.

The same characteristics serve to distinguish some other genera, such as *Pygoplites* and *Centropyges*, including species mainly from the Indo-Pacific. The first of these genera includes *P. diacanthus*, with its yellow body with vertical lines in light blue and black. The second genus has a larger number of species; for example, *C. bicolor* — yellow front and black rear half — and the small *C. argi* (6 cm) — dark blue with orange yellow on the head and on the front part of the belly; it was discovered in 1951 in the western Atlantic and is referred to as the Pygmy Angelfish.

Platacidae. In contrast to the preceding family this family contains only four species, all of which are included in the genus *Platax*. They have been given the common name Bat Fishes because of the remarkable development of the fins which can occur. The body is short and very high, laterally flattened into a rhomboid or an almost disc shape. The mouth is small and many of the teeth have several points. The dorsal and anal fins are high and well developed — particularly in the young — and each begins with short spines; the tail fin is not forked. These fishes live along the coast in the Red Sea, the Indian Ocean and the Pacific, and at times enter the brackish waters of river

Top left: *Platax orbiculans*; the very well developed fins give a characteristic appearance to this fish.
Right: *Euxiphipops xanthometopon*, a multicoloured Indo-Pacific species.

123

Left: *Zanclus cornutus*;
this fish resembles the
Butterfly fishes, but it
is, in fact, related to
Surgeon fishes (see p. 140).
Right: (*Chromis chromis*),
this very common fish is
the only member of
Pomacentridae living in
the Mediterranean.

mouths. It is best to choose young fishes of similar size for aquaria unless there is a great deal of room, because fully grown fishes attain very large sizes. Different species are often confused with one another, and also the fully-grown fish can look entirely different from the juvenile. The young fish, in fact, can have a really fantastic appearance due to the development of the large dorsal and anal fins (and sometimes the pelvic fins too) that can grow longer than the body itself. *Platax orbicularis* and *P. teira* are often kept in large aquaria: the first can measure up to 50 cm in depth. *P. pinnatus* has a red rim running along the back and the edges of the fins.

Pomacentridae. These fishes enjoy the same popularity as the Butterfly fish, not only among aquarists, who refer to them as the Damsel fishes or 'Demoiselles', but also among people who are interested in marine fauna in general. They are small but with great variations of coloration; the young are especially attractive. Many pomacentrids can be listed amongst the most beautiful inhabitants of tropical coastal waters. The body is oval in shape; the dorsal fin is very long with a series of sharp spines anteriorly; the tail fin has two lobes. The snout is short and rounded, the mouth small with teeth of different shapes; the scales are ctenoid and the lateral line is interrupted. These small fishes are popular aquarium specimens. They are easy to keep and given the right conditions, they can breed in captivity. Their diet is either carnivorous or omnivorous. They have very interesting habits: they have a strong territorial instinct and can be aggressive.

The single species belonging to this family in the Mediterranean, *Chromis chromis*, is also found along the adjacent coasts. It is about 12 cm long and as a young fish is vividly coloured in blue, changing to dark brown when fully grown. It is very commonly found along the coasts, living in large shoals. Two species related to it, *C. caeruleus* – of the Indo-Pacific – and *C. cyaneus* – of the western Atlantic – are, as their names imply, brightly coloured in blue. *Abudefduf saxatilis* is bigger (18 cm) and has five vertical black stripes going across the blue-grey sides; it is commonly found in all oceans. It is gregarious when young, but develops solitary habits as it matures. This fish is adaptable to aquarium life, and the same can be said of the several species of the genera *Pomacentrus* and *Dascyllus*, which are major components of the marine fauna of the coral reefs. *Pomacentrus leucostictus* (10 cm) lives in the Caribbean Sea; it is blue

124

Top left: Above:
Dascyllus trimaculatus.
Below: *Amphiprion
ephippium*.
Top right: *Chromis
caeruleus*, a fish living on
the coasts of the Indian
and Pacific Oceans.
Bottom: A small shoal of
Clown fishes or
Amphiprion percula which
live in association with large
tropical sea anemones.

on the upper part of the body and yellow on the remainder. *Dascyllus aruanus* is a little smaller; it is white with a few broad black stripes, either oblique or vertical, across the body. *D. trimaculatus* is all black with three white dots on the head and is quite unmistakable. Both these species can be found from the Red Sea to the Pacific, together with *Amphiprion* or Clown Fishes which are very pretty and have the most interesting and unusual habits. Their association with some tropical sea anemones such as *Discosoma* and *Stoichactis* is, in fact, famous. All the species of this family can live and hide in the venom-laden tentacles of the large sea anemones with complete immunity: some experiments carried out by scientists suggests that the Clown fish secrete neutralizing mucus from their skin that protects them from the sting of the sea anemones. Usually a sea anemone gives shelter to a pair of fishes that make their nest and lay eggs (100 to 140 at a time) close to its base. This is a specific symbiosis, in that only determinate species of Sea Anemone and Clown fish are associated. Only some Clown fishes can be kept in aquaria because not all of them adapt equally well. The best known is perhaps *A. percula*; it has broad alternate white and orange bands across the body and only grows about 10 cm long. There are some larger species, as, for example: *A. ephippium*, bright red with a black patch on the back; *A. polymnus* and *A. sebae* — confusingly similar to each other — about 12 cm long and black or reddish brown with two white vertical lines, one on the back of the head, and one on the middle of the body. *Premnas biaculeatus* — from the Indian Ocean and the Pacific — also lives in symbiosis with large sea anemones: this fish has a characteristic spine below each eye; it is red with the three vertical white bands.

Labridae. These fishes (Wrasses) are similar to the pomacentrids but have a slightly longer body and cycloid scales. They have two nostrils on each side of the head (in common with the majority of fishes) instead of one (as in the Damsel fishes); the tail fin is not forked, and there is one dorsal fin, with sharp spines at the front. The lips are often thick (as the name implies), and the size of the fish is generally much larger than that of the Damsel fishes. Wrasses often have a beautifully coloured body and their appearance varies according to age and sex. Sex changes are not rare in certain species of this family. All are strictly marine fishes and live in coastal zones. They are plentiful in tropical

and temperate regions. They roam in amongst rocks, algae, in *Posidonia* beds, and coral reefs: many species live among colonies of coral. Often they hide at the bottom — for example in the gravel or sand of the aquarium — at night, or they sleep propped against rocks. Their colours seem to fade at night, a phenomenon also observed in other fishes. They are carnivorous or omnivorous. Parental care is left to the male fish, which builds a nest with bits of algae, and guards the eggs, at times in a most aggressive way. Many Mediterranean species build nests. There are no special requirements when keeping Labridae in aquaria, apart from choosing young fish or the smaller species; these make, in fact, good ornamental aquarium specimens. Wrasses have many representatives in the Mediterranean and are amongst the most colourful fishes living there. Some of these species are confined to the Mediterranean, others are found in the Atlantic, too.

Labrus turdus (growing to more than 40 cm), has variable coloration: often it has a green back and sides (with or without a longitudinal silvery-white stripe) and the underside is covered in stripes or patches of yellow, orange and red. This species is a protogynus hermaphrodite — that is, the young

specimens are all female and change into males without variation in colour. However, the Cuckoo Wrasse (*L. bimaculatus*), common in Italian seas and British waters, undergoes a spectacular transformation: the female fish is red with few black spots on the back towards the tail, while the male is blue and yellow with varying patterns. Smaller in size and not easy to distinguish from each other are the various species of the genus *Symphodus*. These fishes have thicker bodies than the previous Wrasses and the preoperculum has a series of fine teeth. They live in large numbers in amongst the *Posidonia* beds in which some build nests. The little *S. rostratus* (not over 8 to 10 cm) has a peculiar long thin snout, the upper part having a concave outline; the coloration is extremely varied (reddish, olive, green etc.). *S. roissali* is slightly larger and equally varied in colour and it has from two to five black spots on the dorsal fin. Still larger are *S. mediterraneus* (12 to 15 cm) and *S. tinca* (30 cm): the former has a black spot at the base of the pectoral fins and on the tail end of the body; the latter is distinguished by the very thick lips and the blue and red speckles on the dorsal and anal fins and on the tail fin.

Wrasses of the genera *Coris, Thalassoma* and *Halichoeres* include a large

Left: *Symphodus ocellatus* (the colour is not always red).
Right top: *Labrus turdus*.
Below: *Symphodus tinca*, a colourful species of Wrasse living in the Mediterranean.

127

number of species, distributed in the tropical zones of all oceans. They are highly colourful and their appearance is often eye-catching. The Rainbow Wrasse (*Coris julis*) is a very common Mediterranean fish, often found in rocks and amongst *Posidonia* growths. The young fish, all of which are female, have a brown or reddish back and a yellow lateral stripe: older fishes (up to 25 cm) are brown, greenish or reddish on the upper part of the body, with a red or orange band along the side which becomes wavy at the edges: these are the male fishes. This species is found in the Mediterranean and also along a good part of the eastern Atlantic coastline. *C. gaimardi* —an inhabitant of the Pacific and Indian Oceans—has marked colour variations according to age. The younger fishes are greatly valued by aquarists: they have a brick-red coloured body with some large white patches edged with black. The adult fishes, on the other hand—up to 15 cm long—are less attractive: they are olive brown with small blue dots and lines. This species lives exclusively among coral formations. The genus *Thalassoma* has larger scales than *Coris*; and has eight (instead of nine) spiny dorsal fin-rays and the outer rays of the tail fin are elongate, giving the fin a moon-shape. One of

Opposite page: Top:
Symphodus roissali.
Centre: *Symphodus
mediterraneus.*
Bottom: *Symphodus
cinereus.*
All these Wrasses are
common in the coastal
zones of the Mediterranean
and have a varied
coloration.
Right: A male Rainbow
Wrasse (*Coris julis*).

This page: Top: Female
Rainbow Wrasse (*Coris
julis*).
Centre: Rainbow Wrasse in
the course of sex change.
Bottom: Male Rainbow
Wrasse. As in other species
of this family, this fish
species undergoes a change
of sex, accompanied by
variation in colours. All
individuals are female first
and then male.

The many colours of an adult Peacock Wrasse (*Thalassoma pavo*).

the most elegant-looking fishes of the Mediterranean Sea is the Peacock Wrasse (*T. pavo*) which is found in the warmer parts of the Mediterranean and along the African coast of the Atlantic. This fish is found on rocky bottoms, often together with *C. julis*, and both fish change sex as they grow. The young fish, which are all female, are greenish with a few light-coloured vertical lines and a marked black spot at the base of the dorsal fin: the larger fishes (males) have a bright green body and blue wavy lines across the head which is red. *T. lunare* (Red Sea and Indian Ocean) is very similar. *T. bifasciatum* (up to 12 cm in length) is extremely prolific in the Western Atlantic (Caribbean Sea, Gulf of Mexico, Florida and Bermuda). Its young form part of the colourful display of tropical fish life at the bottom of oceanic waters, roaming in small groups. They are yellow with a blackish stripe along the side and are female or immature males. The 'super males' are more numerous and are commonly called 'Blue Heads' because of their coloration.

A common Wrasse found in the Indo-Pacific from the Red Sea to Polynesia is *H. centriquadrus*, with a typical chequered pattern on the whitish underside, formed by series of little brown dots. *Labroides dimidiatus* is a more interesting species because of its habits. It is small (only 10 cm), pretty fish, coloured blue with a broad band of a darker shade of blue, which runs along its full length from the snout to the tail fin. This is a typical 'cleaner fish'. It lives among the coral reefs and has sedentary habits; various species of fish, large as well as small, come to it to be relieved of parasites or to have a piece of diseased or damaged fin or skin removed. *Labroides* attends to this task with great zest, cleaning not only its patients' skin, but also their gill cavities and the insides of their mouth. This behaviour can be observed in the aquarium. Some other fishes have cleaning habits, for instance young specimens of *Thalassoma bifasciatum*, mentioned above. *L. dimidiatus* is commonly found from the Red Sea to Hawaii.

Throughout the same vast area *Cheilio inermis* is found; easily identified by its very slim body — up to 40 cm long — and with very variable coloration (green, blue, brown, or yellow). No less characteristic is *Gomphosus varius*. It has a long, thin, tube-like snout, measures about 20 cm and shows a marked sexual dimorphism: the male fishes are green, females are brown. This species is found from the Red Sea to the Pacific Ocean (Hawaii and

Opposite page: *Bodianus rufus*, one of the most beautiful members of the Wrasse family.

131

Tahiti). The members of the genus *Hemigymnus* are native to the Indian Ocean and the Pacific; they have thick lips and brightly contrasting colours. *H. melapterus* – 30 cm in length – is bicoloured: the back half is dark brown, while the front half is almost white. *H. fasciatus* – also found in the Red Sea – has a yellowish head with wavy purple lines, while the rest of the body is dark brown with white slanted lines across. The varied species of the genus *Cheilinus* also belongs to the Indian Ocean and the Pacific and is distinguished by an interrupted lateral line and a characteristic green and red coloration.

Among the American species of this family *Bodanius rufus* and *Lachnolaimus maximus* deserve mentioning. The first, growing to 50 cm, is found in the Caribbean Sea and the Gulf of Mexico, around Florida and the Bermuda Islands; it has very characteristic coloration as a rule, being red on the upper of its front half and yellow on the rest of the body. The second species is bigger (90 cm) and roams mainly among the masses of Gorgonians in coastal waters from the southern United States to the Caribbean Sea. It can be easily identified by the high and compressed body, the pointed snout, and high dorsal fin – with the first three spiny rays much

longer than the rest. The coloration is varied but is mainly red to maroon with dark or light coloured markings. The Razor fish (*Xyrichthys novacula*) is a Wrasse with a distinctive look, and very different from all the fishes already described. It has an extremely compressed body, which is very thin along the edges of the back and the ventral surface: the head is high and has an almost vertical profile at the front. It has delicate colours, differing according to age and sex: the younger individuals (female) are pink; the larger ones (males, as these fishes change sex with age) are greenish. There are some light blue lines along each side of the head. This species can grow to over 20 cm in length. It is common in the Mediterranean and also found in the Atlantic, both west and east. It prefers a sandy bottom, where it likes to bury itself. It adapts well to the aquarium.

Scaridae. All members of this family have the common name of 'Parrot fishes'. There are two reasons for this name: the brightness and variety of colours and the stout 'beak' that in reality does not protrude. The beak consists simply of the two strong jaws and a pair of plates on each, formed by series of fused teeth. The surface of these plates has, therefore, the appearance of a mosaic. Also

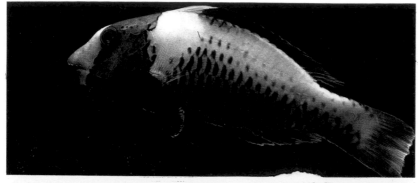

Left top: Parrot fish (juvenile coloration of *Chlorurus bicolor*). Below: young *Coris gaimardi*. Right: *Coris gaimardi* (adult fish).

characteristic are the large pharyngeal bones that bear numerous molar-like teeth, adapted to crunching hard bodies. The scales are large and cycloid, the fins are basically similar to those found amongst the Wrasses. The size of these fish varies from medium to large (they can reach a metre in length) and therefore only juvenile fishes are normally kept in aquaria. Parrot fishes live along coastal zones of tropical seas and are abundant near coral formation; they are, in fact, typical 'coral fishes'. Their diet is essentially herbivorous. Only one species (*Sparisoma cretense*) lives in the Mediterranean Sea: it measures up to 50 cm, and its basic colours are red or greenish. The Atlantic species of Parrot fish are more brightly coloured: for instance, *Scarus caeruleus* — which is a vivid blue — measuring up to 90 cm; and *S. taeniopterus*. There are also the multicoloured *S. ghobban* and the no less common *S. harid* — pink or pale blue — which come from the Pacific and Indian Oceans.

Uranoscopidae. The only Mediterranean representative of this family — which has a strikingly characteristic appearance — is the curious Star Gazer (*Uranoscopus scaber*). Its strange look is due to a large box-like head with a wide mouth at the front edge, and eyes placed so that they look upwards. Immediately behind the head there are two spines pointing backwards. There are two dorsal fins, the first of which is very short and consists of only a few short spiny rays. The pelvic fins are placed well forward, even under the throat. The tail fin is triangular in shape. This fish is 25 cm long; its coloration is plain. It lives on the bottom where it buries itself, only leaving the eyes and perhaps a small section of the back and dorsal fin exposed. It is carnivorous.

Trachinidae. This family have a very similar biological and structural resemblance to the previous one and includes the *Trachinus* species (Weevers) which have a rather bad reputation due to their extremely venomous spines. A very pointed spine placed horizontally above the operculum pointing backwards is, in fact, a family characteristic. It has a venom-producing gland at its base. The venom is injected into the victim through the spine itself. The black spiny rays of the first dorsal fin are equally poisonous.

The Weevers are common in the Mediterranean basin, where four species are found, all of them also occurring in the east Atlantic. The members of this family are benthic (i.e. sea-bed dwellers) and live on sandy or muddy bottoms, buried up

to their eyes, with only the venom-bearing spines raised above the bottom. They are carnivorous and live on fishes and invertebrates. They live well and relatively long in aquaria, provided they have sand or gravel at the bottom under which they can hide.

Trachinus draco — up to 40 cm long — has several yellow and blue lines slanting across the side. It is a very common species. In winter it leaves coastal waters and goes down to a greater depth of 100 m or more. *T. araneus* and *T. radiatus*, also common along the Mediterranean shores, are covered by brown patches or dots. *Echiichthys vipera*, which does not grow more than 14 cm long, is the smallest of the Weevers; it can be distinguished from those mentioned above, because it does not have the small spines above the eyes which are common to all other Weevers. Notwithstanding its small size, it can inflict one of the most painful stings.

Blenniidae. Like the families just mentioned these fishes also belong to the large order, of Perciformes, in spite of the difference in their appearance. The skin is completely scaleless and covered with mucus; (in the Italian regions they are called 'Bavose' meaning slimy). The dorsal fin is long and without stiff spines, the tail fin is usually blunt-edged, and the pelvic fins are placed virtually under the throat, as in the Weevers. The species vary in colour and in the eventual development of small tentacles on the head. They are always small in size. These fishes live in coastal zones, at various depths, but always close to hiding places either at the bottom or under rocks and in crevices on the shore. They are often seen propped up on their pelvic fins. Their diet consists of algae and small invertebrates. The eggs are laid on stones, among algae or in empty sea-shells. Blennies adapt extremely well to aquarium life. There are numerous species from the Mediterranean Sea. *Blennius gattoruggine*, the Tompot Blenny — 30 cm long — is, perhaps, the biggest of them. It has a much branched tentacle over each eye; it is brown, with darker vertical lines and spots, resulting in a complex coloration which helps to merge with the surroundings. *E. tentacularis* is smaller and has long tentacles above the eyes, while *B. sanguinolentus* has very short tentacles. *B. pavo* is much smaller and has a characteristic sexual dimorphism: the head of the male grows much higher because of a fatty crest which grows along the top of it. This small fish (10 cm) favours sea beds of sand mixed with mud and strewn with seaweed-covered rocks, and is very resistant to variations in

Uranoscopus scaber (right) is a characteristic Mediterranean fish that hides in the sea-bed (see left), ready to catch its prey.

135

temperature and salinity. It can be considered one of the 'ornamental' fishes, as the greenish body is covered with attractive iridescent blue markings.

Many small Blennies are found along the Mediterranean coasts. *B. sphinx* only grows to 7 cm; it has tentacles above the eyes and several greenish-brown vertical bands. *B. canevai* (7 cm) has no tentacles, is brown with a network of light-coloured markings, and has a characteristic yellow head. *B. ocellaris* lives deep down on sandy sea-beds; it grows to a length of 20 cm and is easily recognized because the anterior part of the dorsal fin grows much higher and has a characteristic black blotch surrounded by a white and blue halo. The Blenny, *Aspidontus taeniatus*, is an Indo-Pacific species which bears a mimetic resemblance to the Wrasse known as the 'cleaner fish'.

Many of the tropical blennies constitute a large group with common characteristics, such as very small and numerous movable teeth. Many hop agilely on dry rocks and, because of the tightly closed, narrow gill slits, are able to survive out of water for a relatively long time. *Salarias fasciatus* — 10 cm in length — has a dorsal fin of uniform height, and an anal fin with elongated first rays; its coloration is green. *Lophalticus kirki* is of strange appearance, due to the fleshy crest on the head which is restricted at the top. It is brown with many darker vertical stripes and grows up to 9 cm in length. These two Blennies live in the Red Sea and the Indian Ocean, and the genus *Salarias* is also found in the west Pacific. Similar in size and habitat is *Ecsenius bicolor* which has two little tentacles on the head.

The clinids are a family of fishes (having scales) next in classification to the Blennies. *Clinetrachus argentatus*, a pretty little fish seldom reaching 10 cm in length, is the only Mediterranean representative of this family. It has a variable coloration (green, brown, red; always with large whitish-silvery patches along the sides). The dorsal fin is heavily concave in shape.

Gobiidae. This is an enormous series of either small or minute fishes (it includes one of the smallest vertebrates: 9 mm in length) that are popularly kept in aquaria, where they settle well. They are attractive because of their colours, and very interesting for some of their unusual habits. The body is rather elongated, sometimes scaleless; the lateral line is absent. Gobies have two dorsal fins and the tail fin is rounded. Very often they have characteristic pelvic fins joined together in

the shape of a single fan, long and rounded. Their exceptional variety of environmental and behavioural features is a main source of interest in these fishes. Gobies live along the shores of temperate and tropical seas; some penetrate inland and are found in the brackish water of lagoons, others can be found in fresh water. Their diet consists of invertebrates and they lay their eggs on the bottom.

There are many Mediterranean species of Gobies (some confined to this basin), and they are commonly called 'Ghiozzi' in Italian. They vary considerably in colour and size, but are by no means easily distinguished. *Gobius niger, G. paganellus, G. cruentatus* – all extending as far as the European Atlantic coast – are amongst the larger species and reach about 15 cm. The general colour of the body is brown, with darker markings. *G. cruentatus* (i.e. 'blood-stained') has characteristic red patches around the mouth and at the side of the head. This is strictly a sea-water species, while the other two can be found in brackish waters as well. *G. niger* has a high first dorsal fin, with rays that extend to form filaments. The three Gobies just described are often found on bottoms of different types. Many other Gobies associate with animals of various kinds. *G. bucchichi* is found

in symbiosis with the sea anemone, *Anemonia sulcata*, with a relationship similar to that existing between the Amphiprions and the large tropical sea anemones. *Lotillia graciliosa* – a small maroon fish with lighter patches and with a vivid ocellate orange spot on its first dorsal fin – was first observed in 1960 living in the Red Sea, in association with small shrimps (alphaeids), sharing the nests that the crustaceans hollow out in the sand for themselves. Several species of *Smilogobius*, which are found in the Indo-Pacific have similar habits.

Gobiodon rivulatus has a maximum length of 5 cm. It has a large head and bright coloration in red, reddish-brown or green with red stripes. *G. citrinus* is similar in shape, but – as the name indicates – is yellow. These two Gobies love to hide among corals and are widespread in the Red Sea across to the Pacific Ocean. *Lythrypnus dalli* (3 cm) is red with a few blue vertical lines, and lives in Californian waters. *Elacatinus oceanops* (9 cm) is blue-black with a light blue stripe along each side; its home is the tropical zone of the west Atlantic.

The Mud Skippers, which are sometimes classified as Gobies but which could be defined as a family, are, without a doubt, among the strangest fishes. Their appearance is unmistak-

Left top: *Blennius tentacularis*.
Below: *Blennius sphinx*.
Right: A colourful small tropical fish, roaming amongst coral.

137

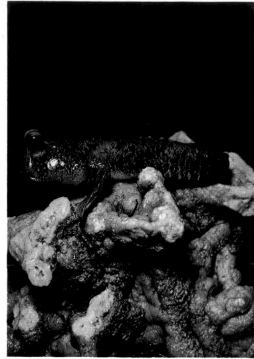

Left: *Gobius paganellus* and many other species of Goby are very common in the Mediterranean. Right: A Mud Skipper (*Periophthalmus*), strange fishes of tropical coastal zones.

Opposite page: *Siganus vulpinus*, a fish living in Indonesian waters and Oceania, noteworthy for its remarkable and strange coloration and its elongated snout.

able: the eyes are set high on the head and close together, are protruding and very mobile; the pectoral fins are 'pedunculate' and seem to be almost arm-like; the body is brown or black, sometimes speckled with white dots, while the fins are more colourful: this fish reaches a maximum length of 20 cm. Several Indo-Pacific species have been confused with *Periophthalmus koelreuteri*: there is *P. papilio* present in West Africa. These strange-looking tropical fishes live close to the shores, and are particularly common in mangrove swamps. They come out of the water and hop about with great skill, surviving in the air for a long time.

Siganidae. The shape of the snout in this group of fishes, of which there is only one genus (*Siganus*) has earned them the name 'Rabbit fishes' which is, however, not very apt. The body is rather unremarkable, but the mouth is small and well equipped with incisor-like small teeth, used to tear at the seaweed which forms the main diet of these fishes. Also character-istic are the many spines in its fins: it has 13 spines in the dorsal fin; 7 in the anal, and 2 in each pelvic fin. These rays can all inflict painful wounds. All the species belong to the tropical regions of the Indo-Pacific. Two of them, though, have penetrated from

the Red Sea to the eastern Mediter-ranean through the Suez Canal, and they are now well established; they are *S. rivulatus* and *S. luridus*. *S. vulpinus*, about 20 cm long, is light brown with a bold dark stripe on the head and another on the front of the body; it is found in the seas of the East Indies.

Acanthuridae. The name of this family (from the Greek and meaning 'spiny tail') illustrates the character-istic which is constant in its members: i.e. the presence of a sharp scalpel-like spine placed in a narrow slot at each side of the tail which is freely erectile. These fishes have minute scales, a long dorsal fin, a tail fin which has either two lobes or is moon-shaped, and a small mouth with thin sharp teeth. They all live in tropical seas near the coast and are plentiful on coral reefs. They are strictly vegetarian. Because of their coloration, which sometimes attains a rare elegance, these fishes could make excellent aquarium specimens, but, quite apart from the question of their size (rather large), they are rather delicate and difficult to maintain. The species of *Acanthurus* well deserves the common name of 'Surgeon fishes', as they can inflict deep cuts with the sharp blades they have at the side of the tail.

A. caeruleus — about 30 cm in length — is common in the tropical Atlantic; the

Left: *Acanthurus lineatus.*
Right: *Acanthurus leucosternon.* These are Surgeon fishes, a group particularly elegantly coloured.

Opposite page: Top: *Paracanthurus hepatus:* An Indo-Pacific species which displays various colours, arranged in a very characteristic pattern. Below right: *Zebrasoma veliferum.*

young fish is yellow; while the adults are light blue with thin, darker blue lines running along the sides. Among the various species in the Indian Ocean and the Pacific, *A. triostegus* (25 cm) is distinguished by the vertical lines which stand out on an olive-green or light brown background. Even more beautiful, however, are *A. lineatus,* so called because of the numerous blue lines with black edges along the body, and *A. leucosternon,* which is larger (30 cm), and brilliantly coloured: the body is blue, the head black, the underside white, and the tail fin yellow. *Paracanthurus hepatus,* with a large black patch on the blue body, also belongs to the Indian and Pacific Oceans — and is similar to the two species mentioned.

Very different is the shape of *Zebrasoma,* which has a more prominent snout and shortened body. All the members of this genus belong to the Indo-Pacific. The splendid *Z. veliferum,* which reaches 40 cm in length, has very high dorsal and anal fins, adorned with multicoloured dots and lines, as are its sides. *Z. flavescens* is smaller and yellow. *Z. xanthurum* is one of those individuals that adopt different coloration according to location. In the Red Sea it is purple, but elsewhere it is either yellowish or red-brown. The tail fin, however, is always

yellow, as its scientific name implies. The Surgeon fishes of the genus *Naso* are less eye-catching in coloration, but have a strange, even grotesque. shape, with a protruding — in some cases even long — 'horn' on the head, which really resembles a nose. *N. lituratus* — greenish or grey, with yellow lines across the head — grows to 45 cm long and is found, as the other related species, in the Indian and Pacific Oceans.

The family Zanclidae is related to the Surgeon fish family and only has two species: *Zanclus cornutus* and *Z. canescens.* These fishes resemble the Butterfly fishes in their general shape. The body is laterally flattened and deep, with high dorsal and anal fins; the snout is prominent, with small mouth and teeth; between the eyes there is a more or less prominent bump. Both species — also called 'Moorish Idols' — are similar and are found in the Indo-Pacific. They grow to a length of 20 cm or a little more. They have an eye-catching pattern. Zanclus feed on seaweed and small invertebrates. They are very sensitive to changes in environment.

Scorpaenidae. Although they are placed in a separate order (Scorpaeniformes), these fishes are very similar to the Perciformes, not least for the strong spines in their fins. However,

140

they have a distinct feature of the head skeleton: a thin bony plate runs beneath the eye, from the front of the suborbital bone (of which it is an extension) to the preoperculum. Scorpaenids have very varied appearances, often extremely odd and most unattractive. The head is large, craggy and well equipped with spines; the mouth is large. Some have bright colours, but more often their coloration is dull and helps them to merge with the background. They inhabit temperate and tropical seas in shallow or medium depths; most live close to the bottom and usually hide amongst algae, rocks and coral. They are carnivorous. The points on the spiny fin rays constitute their means of offence and defence, as they are connected to glands with secretions which are venomous.

The Scorpionfishes are typical of this group and several species are found in the Mediterranean basin. The largest of these (50 cm in length) is the Red Scorpionfish (*Scorpaena scrofa*) which is well endowed with flaps of skin on the sides and the head, including the jaws. The Black Scorpionfish (*Scorpaena porcus*) is much smaller (never more than 25 cm). In actual fact this fish is generally brown with lighter and darker spots. Both these fishes, and all related species, are able

to camouflage themselves extremely well, as is shown by specimens kept in the aquarium, which are difficult to see. These two Scorpionfish, which are also found in the eastern Atlantic, differ in environmental requirements. In its adult state, the red species lives on muddy bottoms at a depth of about 10 m, while the black species is always found in much shallower waters amongst rocks and *Posidonia* beds. *S. grandicornis,* an exotic species, takes its name from the long skin tentacles growing above the eyes: it is indigenous to the tropical zones of the western Atlantic.

The members of the genus *Pterois* have for several years been familiar to aquarists. They are typical scorpaenids, all belonging to the Indo-Pacific basin, which are often known as 'Lion fishes'. The magnificent *P. volitans* (up to 35 cm long) has enormously enlarged fins that give this fish an unreal, fairy-tale appearance; the pectoral fins have long separate rays and the spines of the dorsal fin are long and free of the membrane for most of their length. It has long tentacles above each eye. It is white in colour with vertical black and brown lines of varying thickness along the body. This fish is commonly distributed from the Red Sea to the Pacific Ocean. Its spines are lethal, as

they have venom-producing tissue at the base and along their length. This venom has some affinity with that produced by snakes. A wound causes immediate and very acute pain with varying consequences. *P. radiata* has smaller proportions (20 cm) and is recognized by the vertical white lines, contrasting with the brownish-red background, which cross the body and branch on the back. In the related genus, *Dendrochirus*, the rays of the pectoral fin are joined by a membrane in the normal way. *D. zebra* and *D. brachypterus*, both only reaching about 20 cm in length, have the whole of the body, including fins, speckled in black, red, white and grey. All the Scorpionfishes described here adapt well in aquaria.

Totally different in appearance is the Stone fish (*Synanceia verrucosa*) a scorpaenid worth mentioning, even though — because of its morphological characteristics and its way of life — it cannot be recommended as an aquarium specimen. The appearance of this fish can only be described as monstrous: short body, enormous mouth, brown coloration, merging with the surrounding seaweed and sand. It usually lies perfectly still at the bottom resembling a stone wedged between rocks or coral. It is about 30 cm long and is found in the Indian

Left: *Dendrochirus zebra*.
Below: *Pterois radiata*.
These species of
Scorpionfish live in the
Indo-Pacific. Their dorsal
fins have long and sharp
spines capable of inflicting
very painful and venomous
stings.

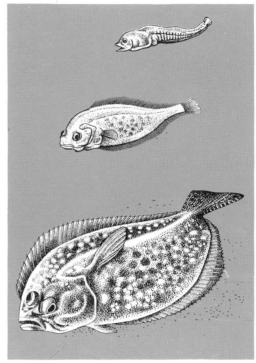

and Pacific Oceans near the coast, and is often inadvertently trodden on. The spines are short and, except for the tip, are entirely covered by skin, the base of which contains the venom glands. A wound from a spine causes excruciating pain and can result in death: the Stone fish is considered to be the most venomous (or greatest venom-producing) of all fishes. Some other strange-looking scorpaenids are also part of the tropical fish fauna. The small *Tetraroge barbata* (10 cm) — Indian Ocean and the Pacific — is brown. It is kept in aquaria. Similar to it is *Amblyapistus binotatus* (Indian Ocean) which has a dorsal fin even more elevated in the front and a vivid silvery-white patch on each side. *Inimicus japonicus* lives in Japanese seas (as the name implies), and it has an elongated and up-turned snout; the numerous spines of the dorsal fin are almost free of the fin membrane; coloration is brown with the usual camouflage markings of dark lines and dots characteristic of all scorpaenids. *Congiopodus peruvianus* belongs to eastern and western coasts of South America. It is about 20 cm long, a light chestnut brown with darker patches; the dorsal fin is high.

Triglidae. The Gurnards are amongst the best known animals of the Mediterranean fauna. Their appearance cannot be mistaken as they have a very large (almost box-like) head, completely shielded with bony plates covered in ridges and spines. Since, once again, they belong to the order Scorpaeniformes the side of the head skeleton is reinforced with a stout bone beneath the eye. The enlarged pectoral fins are also characteristic, with the three lower rays free of the fin membrane. A series of small spines is often found along the base of the two dorsal fins. The tail fin is concave, but not forked. The Gurnards live on the sea-bed, where they move supporting themselves on the free pectoral rays as if they were little legs or feelers. They feed on crustaceans and other invertebrates. They can produce grunting noises, by contracting their swim-bladder. Some species are kept in the aquarium as their mode of walking' on the bottom is rather unique: but their coloration is plain. *Trigla lucerna* grows to 60 cm; it is reddish or slate grey, with blue pectoral fins which have a black patch speckled in light blue visible on the inside. *Trigloporus lastoviza* is considerably smaller (35 cm) and is distinguished by the numerous thin vertical lines running across the whole length of the body. Its colour is red — lighter on the pectoral fins, which have contrasting light blue markings.

144

As with other Flatfishes the coloration of *Bothus podas* is highly camouflaging.

Unlike the others, *Lepidotrigla cavillone* (no longer than 20 cm) is covered in rather large scales and has short pectoral fins; it is either red or reddish grey with blue pectoral fins: it is found in relatively deep water. All these fishes are very common in the Mediterranean and all but the last, in the eastern Atlantic.

Dactylopteridae. Another remarkable family, which has some affinity with the Gurnards, are the so-called Flying Gurnards (Dactylopteridae). These unusual-looking fishes have a large rectangular head covered by a heavy bone, and huge, multicoloured pectoral fins which, in the past, led people to believe that the fish could fly. The name *Dactylopterus volitans* (given to a tropical species often found in the Mediterranean) is, therefore not appropriate. This fish, up to 50 cm long, is strictly bottom-dwelling and does not live long in an aquarium.

Pleuronectiformes. These are Flatfishes, very valuable to fishermen, but of little interest to aquarists. They have, however, a very unusual structure and for this reason are of great interest to visitors to public aquaria. They are not easily seen, as they like to hide on the bottom, where, thanks to their camouflage colouring, they merge perfectly with the surroundings. When they start to swim they rise horizontally, gently flapping the fins which run along most of the edge of the body. The name Pleuronectidae (i.e. sideways swimmers) is therefore very apt. These fishes have a laterally compressed body, unlike the Rays (flattened dorso-ventrally, that is from above). They lie on the bottom resting on one side (which is colourless): the opposite side (normally brown or grey, with various markings of lines, dots and patches) bears both eyes one beside the other. According to family, the eyes are placed either on the left or on the right side; but there are anomalies, as for instance when the 'blind' side is coloured. This asymmetrical structure is indeed unique and only occurs in the post-larval fish: early larvae have their eyes set in a normal position and swim vertically.

Flatfishes have an oval-shaped body — it can also be oblong or even squarish — covered in cycloid or ctenoid scales, usually small. The fins are generally without spines: the dorsal and anal fins are very long and meet, at times, with the tail fin (which is never forked) thus forming a single edge around the body. There are numerous species distributed in all seas, usually in coastal zones: some reach inland brackish waters or even fresh water. They are sedentary, bottom-dwelling animals. All species are carnivorous.

145

The order Pleuronectiformes contains a number of families of which several members live in the Mediterranean.

Scophthalmidae. Members of the family Scophthalmidae have eyes set on the left side. This family includes the Turbot (*Psetta maxima*), which grows to a metre in length. It has no scales, but the skin is covered by bony plates on the left or eyed side. It eats smaller fishes and invertebrates, and settles well in aquaria. Its relative (*Lepidorhombus bosci*) is smaller (about 30 cm); and smaller still is the Eikström's Topknot (*Phrynorhombus regius*), which only grows about 15 cm long; it has very ctenoid scales. The family Bothidae, too, have eyes set on the left side, and have no lateral line on the blind side. *Bothus podas* is a very common species in the Mediterranean; it reaches a maximum length of 20 cm and has variable coloration. The male fish has eyes set well apart.

The family Pleuronectidae have eyes set on the right side and has only one Mediterranean species: the Flounder (*Platichthys flesus*) which is 50 cm long and greenish brown. It can be found in the northern parts of the Adriatic Sea. The Dab (*Limanda limanda*) belongs to the same family together with the large (3 m long!) Halibut (*Hippoglossus hippoglossus*)

from the North Atlantic. The members of the family Soleidae also have eyes set on the right side; the pectoral fins are either absent or very small. The famous Sole (*Solea solea*) is very common in European seas: it does not grow to more than 30 cm in the Mediterranean basin.

Tetraodontiformes. This is a group of fishes living mainly in warm seas, and having a particular beauty of their own, with unusual shapes and highly coloured bodies. Some of them have become very popular with aquarists. The families that have traditionally been classified as Tetraodontiformes (also called Plectognathi) have some characteristics in common, (for example, strong jaws), but vary considerably both morphologically and biologically so that each family is fairly easily distinguished.

The Trigger fish family (*Balistidae*) is a large group. The formation of the dorsal fin is characteristic. The first dorsal fin is made up of three spines of which the first is elongated, very strong and movable: it is, in fact, also locked so that it cannot be depressed once it is erected, unless the second spine is moved. The second dorsal fin and the anal fin have the same shape and are placed opposite one another. They help the fish to swim by undulating movements. The pelvic fins consist of

The Mediterranean Trigger fish undergoes changes in colour, according to age (Left: juvenile fish; Right: an adult fish).

146

Balistes vetula, common in the tropical Atlantic Ocean.

a single stout and very short spine only just free of the skin. The mouth is small with few, but strong teeth, adapted to crunching shells of molluscs, crustaceans, and sea urchins. The body is covered with a mosaic of bony plates, which are thick and rough, instead of with ordinary scales. These fishes live along tropical shores, often among corals; they have solitary habits and like to rest on one side, much in the manner of Wrasses. They are rather slow and solitary, but display great aggression towards their own species.

Balistes carolinensis is common in the Mediterranean and the Atlantic: it is grey-green with light blue spots and lines. *B. vetula* is more colourful, yellowish with two light blue lines on each side of the head; it is found in all warm regions of the Atlantic, and in the Indian Ocean. *Melichthys niger* (about 20 cm long) is easily identified: the body is black with a contrasting white stripe along the base of the dorsal fin and a similar one along the base of the anal fin. It is found in all tropical seas. *Odonus niger* and *Pseudobalistes fuscus*, which grow to a considerable length (50 cm) inhabit the tropics of the Indo-Pacific from the Red Sea to Oceania. The former is not black, but blue, and it has red teeth instead of the white ones usual to the Trigger fishes. The latter has the body covered with blue spots and stripes on a background which is yellow in the young fishes and orange or green in the adults. The splendid *Balistapus conspicillum* is highly valued: it has large, round patches, either white or yellow, contrasting with the blue-black colour of the body. It can measure 50 cm in length, and lives in the Indian Ocean and some parts of the Pacific. Similar to it are: *B. undulatus* (30 cm), common from the Red Sea to the Pacific Ocean; and *B. aculeatus*, which is replaced by *B. assasi* in the Red Sea. These Trigger fishes are easily recognizable: *B. undulatus* is dark green with several slanted orange-coloured stripes; *B. aculeatus* and *B. assasi* (30 cm) are similar; with some lines of various colours across the yellow background.

The File fish family, *Monacanthidae*, includes fishes very similar to the Trigger fishes, they differ mainly in having minute but rough-edged scales covering the skin — making it very rough — and in the formation of the first dorsal fin which consists of a long spine (often rough-edged) with a second much smaller one. These fishes are tropical and omnivorous. They are more peaceful than the Trigger fishes, but in the aquarium it is wise to avoid the presence of coral,

147

Top: *Pseudobalistes fuscus*.
Centre: *Balistapus aculeatus*.
Below: *Balistapus undulatus*. All these fishes live in tropical waters and are known as Trigger fishes.

Opposite page: One of the most valued specimens for the marine aquarium is *Balistapus conspicillum*, commonly found in the Indian Ocean and the West Pacific.

worms, and other invertebrates as they would be quickly devoured. *Monacanthus ciliatus* is very common throughout the Atlantic Ocean; it is 20 cm long and can change its colour quickly, easily adapting its coloration so as to merge with the background. *Stephanolepis diaspros* is similar in shape and is the only member of this family found in the Mediterranean Sea. It is brown with darker spots and is usually found on sandy bottoms amongst seaweed and in *Posidonia* beds. *Chaetoderma penicilligerum* (Pacific Ocean) has a truly fantastic appearance, with many ramified flaps of skin on its body. *Oxymonacanthus longirostris* is a very characteristic fish found in the Indian and Pacific Oceans. It only grows to 10 cm in length. It has and elongated pointed snout and several series of orange spots standing out from the green and bluish background. The biggest File fish (up to 90 cm long) is *Alutera scripta*, which occurs in all tropical seas. The body is rather elongated and so are the snout and the tail fin. The colour is brown or olive with blue dots and lines. The members of the family Ostraciontidae are called Box fishes and are totally different in appearance on account of the thick, box-like bony carapace which covers the whole body, like a coffin. This consists of

Top left: *Chaetoderma penicilligerum*.
Top right: An example of a juvenile Boxfish (*Ostracion*).
Below: *Oxymonacanthus longirostris*, with the pointed snout characteristic of the File fishes.

Opposite page: Top: *Tetrosomus gibbosus* (side-view and front-view).
Centre: *Lactoria cornuta* (side-view and front-view). The strange multi-sided body gives these fishes a very characteristic appearance.
Bottom: *Anothron hispidus*, one of the most common species of Puffer fishes.

little plates of various colours, set so as to give a mosaic effect: the box has either a triangular or square section and can have spines at each of its corners.

These strange fishes are found in tropical seas, swimming lazily in coastal waters with slow movements of the dorsal and anal fins. They are not easy to keep in the aquarium: they need a constant supply of animal and vegetable food. *Ostracion tuberculatus* is one of the largest and best known species. It measures 45 cm and has a quadrangular sectioned body with smooth corners; the colour is either blue with black spots, or yellow with ocellate light blue marks. *Tetrosomus gibbosus*, which is seldom more than 30 cm in length, is found in the same location as the previous species described. The carapace bears spines and the back is high forming a steep cone. *Lactoria cornuta* is similar in size and has a fantastic appearance: it has long spines sticking out both before and behind the body, including those shaped like horns on each side of the head. This fish, too, belongs to the Indo-Pacific; the colour is either yellow or greenish with darker spots. The tail fin grows with age, and in large individuals it can be as long as the body itself. The three species of *Lactophrys* — which have a triangular

Two views (side and front)
of a Porcupine fish (*Diodon
holacanthus*). The body
is almost completely
covered with spines that
can be erected.

section carapace—are found in the tropical regions of the Atlantic.

Tetraodontidae. The Tetraodontidae are generally known as Puffer fishes. Some details of the freshwater members of this family have already been given in a previous section (page 92), where the beak-like mouth is formed of four strong tooth plates in the jaws, together with the ability of this fish to swallow water until a round body shape is achieved. Bearing in mind their tendency to bite, and that aquarium specimens cannot be of too large a size, they make good pets. Many species can be found in tropical seas. *Arothon hispidus* (about 35 cm long) has a light brown body speckled in white; with a black patch at the base of the pectoral fin, surrounded by yellow lines. It is found from the Red Sea to the Pacific. *Sphoeroides spengleri* is found in large numbers in the warmer Atlantic regions. It measures about 15 cm and is brownish grey with a series of black spots along each side. The large *Lagocephalus lagocephalus* (60 cm long) also shares the same geographical location. It has a grey-blue back and is called Puffer fish in England.

The family Canthigasteridae has only a few species, differing from Tetraodontidae in that they have an elongated snout and laterally compressed body with a ridge along the back. Because of their small size, these fishes are adaptable to aquaria, and are popular with aquarists because of their colourful appearance. *Canthigaster margaritatus*—Indian Ocean and the Pacific—reaches 15 cm in length, is reddish with light blue spots and lines on the body, and has a marked black patch on the back. The few species of Diodontidae are appropriately called Porcupine fishes. The family name—in line with Tetraodontidae—was given in reference to the two 'teeth', i.e. the large plates placed one on each jaw. The body is inflatable—as is that of the Puffer fishes—and, because of the long spines on its body it has a most original appearance. The largest species is *Diodon hystrix*, which grows to 90 cm in length; the spines are used as defensive weapons, and stick out when the fish is inflated. The colour is light brown with numerous dark spots. This fish is found in all tropical seas, and so is the related species *D. holacanthus*, which is smaller (about 30 cm) with a few large black bands slanted across the back. *Chilomycterus schoepfi*, also about 30 cm long, is found in western Atlantic coastal waters from the United States to Brazil. Unlike those of Diodon its spines are much shorter

152

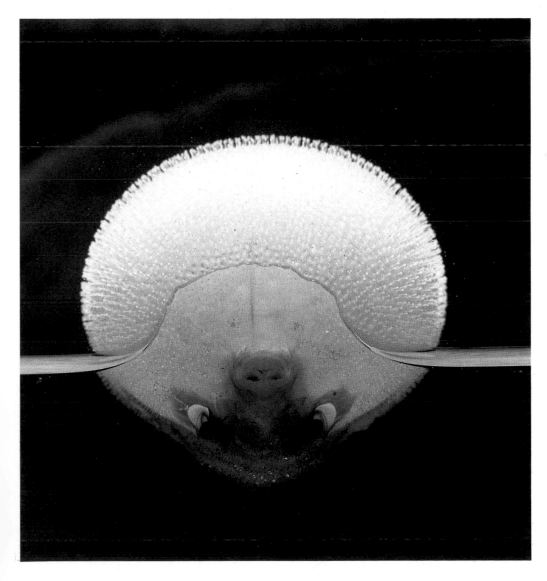

All Puffer fishes, i.e. Tetraodontidae, can fill the body with water or air, so as to become ball-shaped, and then float upside down.

Porcupine fish (*Diodon hystrix*), a fish that is common in tropical seas and capable of puffing itself up in the same way as the Puffer fishes.

and are fixed in place. The colour is greenish with many wavy black lines across. Porcupine fishes are poisonous and of no interest to fishermen.

The Sunfishes also belong to the large class of Tetraodontiformes. These are, in fact, members of the family Molidae, all of which vary in size from large to very large and are therefore unsuited to aquaria. *Mola mola* is one of the giants of the sea. It can grow to over three metres in length and weigh two tons!

Lophiiformes. An older school of naturalists used to place these fishes in the order Pediculati, because the pectoral fins, placed towards the rear, are shaped almost like limbs and appear to be borne on a peduncle. Although many of the species live in the great ocean depths, there are also some found in coastal zones that can be kept in aquaria. They belong to the family Antennaridae (Frogfishes), and their grotesque appearance is quite unmistakable. The body is short and stout; the mouth is large and almost vertical, and the eyes are small. The pectoral fins together with the pelvic fins, which are placed anteriorly on the body, are used for moving along the bottom of the sea, and resemble rudimentary feet. The skin is sometimes scaleless and smooth, sometimes very rough, due to a coating of

small thickly set spines. The Frogfishes are most commonly found in tropical seas, but a few can be found in temperate waters. They live in coastal zones and have sedentary habits, remaining immobile for long periods on the bottom or moving very slowly. However, they are voracious and carnivorous. They are of modest size (10 to 25cm) and have a strange coloration. They can be kept in the aquarium, but they are rather delicate and can devour other animals kept in the same aquarium, including their own kind. *Antennarius ocellatus*, found in all tropical Atlantic regions, is light brown with some large black patches. *Phrynelox zebrinus* (Pacific Ocean) is instead covered in black lines and dots. *Histrio histrio* (the Sargassum fish) settles itself on floating seaweed and is amazingly well camouflaged. The Lophiidae (Angler fishes) from which the whole family takes its name are very different. The Angler fish (*Lophius piscatorius*) is considered one of the most monster-like fishes of them all. It grows to a length of 1·5m and is flattened, with an enormous head and a large mouth filled with sharp teeth. The first dorsal fin has a series of separate rays, the first of which (considerably elongated) has a fleshy flap, which is dangled by the fish to attract its prey.

154

This species of *Antennarius* belongs to a group of bizarre-shaped fishes living mainly in the depths of the ocean.

Amphibians and Reptiles

Although fishes account for the majority of the aquatic vertebrates, they are not the only ones. There are many others and some of these can also be kept in aquaria, both large and small. They are the representatives of two groups, which, although similar superficially, are structurally different: amphibians and reptiles.

The amphibians are particularly bound to an aquatic environment as they usually spend the first period of their life in water, during their larval stage. The numerous tadpoles that dart about in the water of even the most modest pool are, in fact, the larvae of frogs, newts, and toads. The tadpoles have pairs of feathery external gills at the side of the head, while the rest of the body is elongated into a long, flattened tail which is extremely mobile. Gills and tail disappear once the animal completes its metamorphosis and begins its life on dry land: it will then be equipped with lungs for its respiration, and legs for its propulsion. The hind legs are particularly well developed to enable the animal to perform spectacular jumps.

It is quite easy to keep tadpoles in a small aquarium, both in the home or in a classroom, provided there is sufficient vegetation in the water, as the larvae are vegetarian, while the mature animal is carnivorous. The stages of the gradual metamorphosis are interesting to follow and, as any teacher will know, the observation of a live animal is much more valuable for children than any diagram they could find in books.

Newts make attractive pets in aquaria. They are small and have the advantage of having a longer aquatic life, as they remain in water after the metamorphosis has taken place. (The main phases of a newt's life — mating, laying eggs, and metamorphosis — occur in water in which they move with extraordinary ability.) As the tail forms part of the adult animal, newts are classified as Amphibia, Caudata, or Urodela, while the frog and its relatives belong to the order Anura. The general shape of newts, which does not change according to age, rather resembles that of lizards. The colours are often bright, especially in the mating season when the male newts perform a courtship dance before the female displaying their vigour and bright colours. They are carnivorous and devour a large quantity of tadpoles, aquatic insects and other invertebrates. The eggs are attached to water plants. Several species are found in Europe. The largest is the Crested Newt (*Triturus cristatus*), which has a toothed crest along the middle of the back, which

Opposite page: The photographer's camera has caught this small species of freshwater tortoise, displaying its bright colours while swimming.

157

Left: Japanese Giant
Salamander (*Andrias
japonicus*).
Right: One of the many
species of Newts.

is much more developed in the male individuals. Its size is on average about 12 cm in length (although it can occasionally grow to 16 cm); it is black above and yellow with black spots on the underside. The Alpine Newt (*T. alpestris*) is smaller (8 to 10 cm), but more attractive, with a characteristic blue stripe and black dots along the side. It is found in the Alps to a height of 2,500 m, and in the northern parts of the Apennines. Even smaller (5 to 8 cm) is the Common or Smooth Newt (*T. vulgaris*) which is found in much of Europe, and the Italian Newt (*T. italicus*) from central and southern Italy: these are yellow with black stripes and spots.

The Axolotl (*Ambystoma tigrinum*) is a much larger exotic newt, and owes its fame amongst naturalists to the curious phenomenon called neoteny. It occurs when an animal becomes sexually mature and breeds while still in the larval state, in which case the external gill system is retained, enabling the fully developed animal to spend the rest of its life in the water. The Alpine Newt can be neotenous.

The Axolotl (its name originates in Mexico) is black with numerous yellow marks; albino individuals occur which are light in colour. The eastern regions of the United States and Mexico are the habitat of this amphi-

bian. Its larvae are easily reared in an aquarium with plenty of vegetation, provided that some meat or pieces of fish are also added. For years they have been displayed as specimens in public aquaria or kept in laboratories, where the Axolotl serves as an experimental animal.

Many other amphibians are also commonly used in biological experiments. The African Clawed Toad (*Xenopus laevis*) — easily identified as an anuran — is one of these. It is about 8 cm long, brown in colour though lighter on the belly; it has small horny tips to the end of its toes, similar to claws. This animal, indigenous to equatorial Africa, does well in aquaria and breeds freely, the eggs being attached to plants.

The skin of an amphibian is thin, smooth and wet, due to the secretion of numerous glands. Reptiles, on the other hand, are adequately protected by scales and bony (or horny) plates of varying thickness. All these animals breathe by means of lungs, even though they live in the water, and for this reason they need to surface or come on to dry land from time to time. When keeping any of them in an aquarium, it is necessary to cater for this requirement with the provision of stones etc. that are partly above water to provide a dry perch for them.

Opposite page: Top left:
Siren lacertina, an
amphibian characteristic of
North America.
Top right: *Xenopus laevis*,
widely distributed in Africa.
Below: *Herpeton
tentaculatum*, a snake which
lives in brackish waters
(South-East Asia).

As a rule, members of the Crocodile group can only be kept in the large public aquaria. The Alligator (*Alligator mississipiensis*), which lives in the south-eastern United States and grows to a length of 5 m — is often reared in aquaria. Various species of turtles, especially the smaller and more colourful ones, are much more popular amongst aquarists. Characteristic of all these animals, which form a well-defined order of reptiles, is the shell, which consists of bony plates covered by a horny layer and forming an arched 'carapace' over the back and a large, flat 'plastron' under the belly. The head, legs and tail are covered by horny scales. Also horny is the covering of the jaws and this acts as a substitute for teeth.

The aquatic species usually have a flatter carapace than their terrestrial relatives: the name 'tortoise' is generally applied to freshwater and dryland species, while marine ones are called 'turtles'. The European Pond Tortoise (*Emys orbicularis*), which grows to a maximum length of 23 cm, is found widely in southern and eastern Europe. It is black or dark brown, with yellow spots and lines. It lives in marshes and lakes and spends a great deal of time in water: it is an excellent swimmer and preys on a variety of animals, including small fishes. It hibernates

The threatening expression of the *Chelydra serpentina* (the Snapper or Snapping Turtle).

at the bottom of the water during winter, emerging in late spring to lay its eggs on the banks. Some North American species, such as *Pseudemys scripta* (commonly called the Red-eared Turtle because of the reddish-orange patch on each side of the head) and the *P. floridana* are much more attractive because of their bright colours. Many very young specimens can be bought; older ones are less popular as they have duller coloration and are inclined to bite. Though carnivorous when young they tend to become omnivorous with age. The giant species *Chelydra serpentina* (reaching almost a metre in length) can only be seen in large public aquaria; it is not very attractive and has extremely strong jaws. It originates from the waters of the United States, and because of its violent habits is called the Snapping Turtle. It leads an amphibious life, frequently found in fresh water where it catches fishes, and the wet borderlands where it hunts reptiles and amphibians.

Many large turtles live in the sea and are commonly found in all oceans, especially in the tropics. Their limbs are shaped like flippers with the front pair much longer than the back. These animals are very good swimmers and feed on fishes, invertebrates and seaweed. They go on to the beach to lay their numerous eggs. The Loggerhead Turtle (*Caretta caretta*), common in the Mediterranean, is found in all seas: it is often seen in marine aquaria and it can reach a length of over 1·25 m.

The snakes together with the lizards are classed under the order Squamata (meaning 'scaled') and include some aquatic species. All members of the family Hydrophiidae are in fact aquatic animals. These species inhabit the Indian and the Pacific Oceans and are well adapted to marine life. Though their colours are very attractive, they are not popular as they are extremely venomous.

The family Colubridae is represented by our well-known Water Biscia or Ringed Snake (*Natrix natrix*), known also as the Grass Snake. It has a black collar-mark usually accompanied by two large white or yellow patches in front of it, and a greenish body with black spots. Females are bigger and can grow to 1·5 m in length. This quite harmless reptile is very common; it feeds mainly on frogs and small fishes, but can swallow larger animals, as the mouth is big and the jaws are capable of disarticulating. It is an excellent swimmer, even though it spends long periods out of the water. It does well in aquaria where it breeds during the spring, laying about ten soft-shelled eggs on dry surfaces.

160

Above: European Pond Tortoise (*Emys orbicularis*). Below: The Loggerhead (*Caretta caretta*) probably the best-known marine turtle.

Freshwater Invertebrates

In large lakes and small ponds, in torrential rivers and trickling streams lives a mass of minute animals, in which adaptation, metamorphosis, and associations can be observed, all of which are complex but of the greatest interest to the student of freshwater animals. In order to know and understand these better, a great deal of research is carried out in the natural environment and also in the laboratory. This research is not limited to fishes and other vertebrates, but is extended to a vast number of invertebrates as well. Some of these are both easy to obtain and maintain and are popular with aquarists as they help to complete a true picture in the aquarium of the lake or river community.

Freshwater invertebrates belong to different zoological types at least five of which are included in species kept in aquaria. They are: arthropods, molluscs, annelids, cnidarians, porifera. Sometimes they appear 'spontaneously', in the sense that the small animals or their eggs are attached to plants that are put in the tank, or hidden in the bottom soil and then appear without the help of our direct intervention. In some cases their unexpected appearance can be anything but welcome: it is important therefore to know the relationship between all members of an aquarium, so that damage to any individual may be prevented, and conflicts avoided. It is advisable to keep invertebrates separately in small aquaria. Some of them are immobile or definitely sedentary, spending their life attached to a submerged object, some are forever moving about: there are some voracious predators, while others spend their whole life eating debris or plants in a most tranquil way. Some species are tough and prolific, others are delicate and require special care; some spend their whole life in water, others leave the water as soon as the larval period is over.

Insects. Arthropods (their most important characteristics are their jointed limbs and segmented bodies) include first of all the insects — by far the most numerous class in the whole of the animal world. These are very important in the general economy of nature, and they are also most interesting to man for practical reasons. There are several different orders of insects which spend either their whole life or the larval stage in water. Among these are the Odonata which include Dragonflies, those beautiful and unmistakable creatures. With two pairs of large and transparent wings, they dart over the water, depositing their eggs. The larvae are wingless and some can only walk

Opposite page: An example of one of the many species of *Hydra*. This is a minute freshwater animal, capable — as it can be seen in the illustration — of reproducing itself by developing a secondary individual.

on the bottom while others swim with snake-like movements of the body. They are ferocious predators, endowed with a strange device to capture their prey; it consists of a hinged structure formed from a fused third pair of jaws with two strong claws at the end. This structure, which is folded back under the head when not in use (it parts the head and is thus known as a 'mask'), is shot out at great speed when the prey is within reach. The larvae attack not only other invertebrates, but also small fishes, and it is wise to take precautions so as to avoid introducing them in an aquarium containing potential victims. The larvae of other insects, such as Mayflies (Ephemeroptera), Stoneflies (Plecoptera) and Caddisflies (Tricoptera) — all of which leave the water once they have matured — are quite harmless. The larvae of Mayflies have external gills along each side of the body, in the form of either little brushes or thin plates and three fine tufts at the end of the abdomen. The larvae of Stoneflies also have lateral gills, but only two abdominal tufts. Even more interesting is the larva of the Caddisfly, which makes a protective case from twigs, stones, leaves etc. stuck together with its own liquid secretion. Only its head and legs stick out from the case. Amongst the Water Bugs, which have a characteristic rostrum (or sucking beak) folded under the head, are some aquatic species that remain in water after metamorphosis. *Nepa cinerea*, which is grey or blackish, is called the Water Scorpion because of the claw-like shape of its legs. *Ranata linearis*, also a Water Scorpion and known as the Stick-insect, is greenish brown, and has an elongated body and thin legs. Both species are very common in ponds where they live on the bottom, and lay their eggs on plants. *Naucoris cimicoides*, which inflicts a particularly nasty bite, has a shiny, oval body; it is a speedy swimmer and captures other insects with its front legs. *Notonecta glauca*, a greenish-yellow variety of Water Boatman, has the strange habit of swimming upside down. For this it uses its hind legs which are longer than the others.

The members of the genus *Hydrometra* and their relatives, including the Water Measurers (*Hydrometra*), Pond Skaters (*Gerris*) etc., deserve a brief mention, although they are of no interest to aquarists. Supported by long, slender legs, they dart across the surface of the water, but never go in. The Coleoptera (Water Beetles) are distinguished by the hard thick skin which is heavily chitinized, and include an immense multitude of insects,

some of which are aquatic, living in both still and running water. *Dytiscus marginalis* (Great Diving Beetle), which is about 30 mm long, has an olive-black oval body with a contrasting yellow edging; the hind legs are broad and flat and are used for swimming. The males are more numerous and have smooth front wings (called elytra), which in many females are covered by parallel grooves. The Great Diving Beetle lives in ponds and streams; it is a ferocious predator. Its larva, which shares the same habits, has an elongate body and powerful, hooked jaws. *Acilius sulcatus* is a much smaller insect with a yellowish-brown body; the females are more numerous and have grooved elytra (those of the male are smooth). The Silver Water Beetle (*Hydrous piceus*) is the largest aquatic European beetle (45 mm); the body is olive-black, smooth and shiny. It moves more slowly than the Great Diving Beetle; in order to breathe it surfaces with the front part of the body above water. It lives in ponds and ditches with plenty of vegetation to which it attaches a whitish cocoon containing the eggs. There are also surface-living types belonging to Coleoptera: e.g. the Whirligig Beetles, such as *Gyrinus natator*, which is no longer than 6 mm. These little creatures, with a shiny

oval body, dark blue in colour, dart across the surface of the water, describing sinuous curves.

We can fully appreciate why aquatic insects arouse so much interest among aquarists, if we consider how numerous and varied they are in form, habit and location, and how they include some species capable of having a direct influence on human life (the larvae of mosquitoes, for instance, live in water). They are extremely easy to keep in small aquaria, and this allows for careful observation and, with it, the opportunity to understand the fascinating life of these small creatures, and their respective relationships to the organisms living in the same environment. Insects (in both the larval and adult stage) are often a favourite diet of fishes (some species of Toothcarp, e.g. *Gambusia*).

Arachnida and Crustacea. Spiders (Arachnida) are extremely common and plentiful land creatures. However they are not excluded from the aquatic world, where there is one particularly interesting species, the Water Spider (*Argyroneta aquatica*). As in other arachnids the Water Spider has no antennae and has eight legs, instead of six as in insects. It measures about 15 mm (excluding the legs) and the female is smaller than the male. It has a brown, hairy body. It lives in ponds

Two examples of Dragonfly larvae; developing wings are visible on the one on the right.

165

and eats other small creatures. It spins a characteristic web (in the shape of a bell) which is anchored to plants, and fills it with air bubbles taken from the water surface. The Water Spider is easily adapted to aquarium life, but it should not be placed with possible predators, i.e. larger insects and fishes. The outer shell, which is hardened with lime salts into a kind of 'crust', explains the name of 'crustacean', defining an enormous class of arthropods which includes so many varied characteristics of shape, size and habits that it is difficult to summarize them briefly. Crustaceans, however, are mainly aquatic and contribute to freshwater as well as to marine fauna. Crabs and lobsters have well-known characteristics. They belong to the group known as decapods (because of their five pairs of legs). The lobsters are identified by the fact that the segments of the body are in two major divisions: the front part (cephalothorax) bears the antennae, the eyes (on stalks), and the legs (jointed as in all arthropods) – with the front pair enlarged and forming pincers. The hind section (abdomen) is segmented and has short legs shaped in a fan. The freshwater Crayfish (*Austropotamobius pallipes*) is found in the rivers and streams throughout most of Europe; it measures about 13 cm and is greenish brown. It prefers cold water and is active at night, taking shelter under stones or in crevices during the day. It is omnivorous and even eats dead animals. The eggs, laid in the autumn, are kept under the abdomen of the female and hatch in the spring. The River Crab (*Potamon edule*) is found especially in central and southern Italy. It is much less aquatic than the Crayfish, as it spends a considerable length of time on dry land, where it stays until it needs to moisten its gills again. It is also more euryhaline than the Crayfish, as it can survive quite a while in sea water. The body consists mainly of the cephalothorax: the abdomen is small, folded underneath and – in the female – it is used to protect the eggs. Both Crayfish and Crab have a series of larval stages as they develop.

A huge number of small to minute crustaceans – quite different from the ones mentioned above – populate the waters and form an important part of the plankton, thus assuming a primary role in the 'food chains' involving other living organisms and ultimately affecting the welfare of mankind as well. These small creatures – only a few millimetres long and included within the group of Entomostraca ('insect-crustaceans') – belong mainly to the two orders Branchiopoda and

Above: The Water Scorpion (*Nepa cinerea*), an insect that catches its prey with the forelegs.
Below: Among the very many species of spiders there are some that live in freshwater.

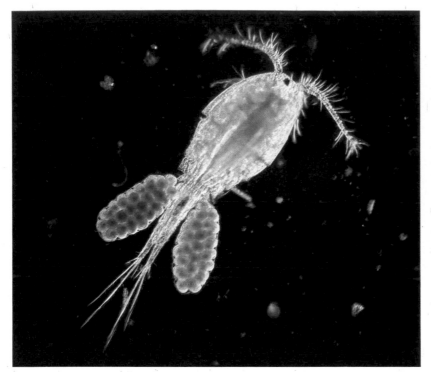

Left: A minute crustacean (*Cyclops*) carrying the egg-sacs.
Right: Water Flea (*Daphnia*) with branched antennae.

Opposite page: One of the several species of Crayfish living in European freshwater.

Copepoda. To the first order belong the Water Fleas (*Daphnia pulex*, etc.) and the Brine Shrimp (*Artemia salina*). The Water Fleas have a shortened body, and branched antennae which are used in swimming. They can breed by parthenogenesis (the eggs developing without fertilization). The Brine Shrimp has a longer and well-segmented body. It is euryhaline and can tolerate salt water, and also provides an excellent source of food for many aquarium specimens.

The second order is commonly represented by *Cyclops*, which has a single eye in the middle of the head, and a body divided into two branches bearing elongate sacs full of eggs.

Molluscs. Although marine molluscs have attractive shells, are more colourful and much more numerous, freshwater species are of great interest to both naturalists and aquarists. They belong to two well-defined classes: Gasteropoda and Lamellibranchiata, which include the majority of molluscs, i.e. a zoological group that contains a large number of species. Gasteropods have a spiral-shaped shell with a soft body which extends outside it. The body includes a head with tentacles, eyes, and mouth. The 'foot' is a flat muscular development of the abdomen and is the structure on which these molluscs crawl about. The snails

— the best known examples of this group — are exclusively terrestrial. There are, however, many varied molluscs to be found crawling on vegetation and stones in streams, ponds, etc. which differ from the ones described above in that the shell is a different shape, and there is only one pair of tentacles with the eyes set underneath. They are, however, similar to snails in that they are 'pulmonates', i.e. they breathe through an internal respiratory cavity and have no gills. These creatures are herbivorous and lay their eggs on aquatic plants or on the bottom.

Many common species belong to the genus *Limnaea*. The largest is the Giant Pond Snail (*L. stagnalis*) (60 mm): the measurement refers to the height of the shell, which is light brown and has a long, pointed spiral. It lives in ditches, ponds and marshes and forms an abundant population. *Stagnicola palustris* is smaller (about 40 mm) and its shell is very similar to that of the last species.

Galba truncatula (6 to 8 mm) is even smaller and is very interesting in that it is the intermediate host for the larval stage of a trematode parasite, the Liver Fluke (*Fasciola hepatica*) which has a rather complicated life-cycle. The Ram's-horn Snail (*Planorbis corneus*) is easily distinguished

168

This page: Above:
Ram's-horn Snail (*Planorbis corneus*).
Below: Freshwater Winkle
(*Viviparus viviparus*).

Opposite page: The Pond
Snail (*Limnaea*), a common
freshwater mollusc.
attaching its eggs to plants
(top right).
Below left: An embryo of
Limnaea.
Below right: A juvenile
individual.

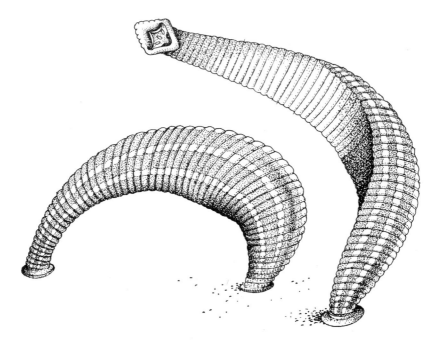

from the Pond Snails (*Limnaea*) by the fact that the spiral of the shell is almost flattened into a disc: it is dark brown and about 30 mm in diameter. The Bladder Snail (*Physa fontinalis*) (10 mm) is identified by a very thin fragile shell, light brown in colour, and a very short spiral. This species is very common in ponds. Some other gasteropods are not pulmonates but retain the method of respiration of the marine species. The Freshwater Winkle (*Viviparus viviparus*) has an olive-brown shell (40 mm), rounded in shape and with darker stripes, bearing a calcareous operculum. It is found both in running and still waters and is ovoviparous. Various species of the genera *Melania* and *Melanopsis*, with long spiral shell, blackish in colour, are popular in aquaria because they like to slide on the sides in search of food and, in so doing, they clean the walls of their coating of green algae. The lamellibranchs are also called bivalves, as the shell is in two halves hinged together along the line of the back of the animal's body, with one valve on the left and one on the right of it. There are only a few freshwater species but these molluscs tend to build up large populations. In the unionids (*Unio glaucinus, U. elongatulus,* etc.) the shell is oblong and thick, with a toothed hinge, it is black on the outside and mother of pearl on the inside. The Swan Mussels (*Anodonta cygnaea, A. piscinalis*, etc.) grow to a length of 200 mm; they have a thin shell, brown on the outside, with a smooth hinge. These molluscs live at the bottom, moving about on the 'foot' which protrudes ventrally like a fleshy tongue between the valves. They remain more or less hidden in the sand or mud.

Other freshwater invertebrates. Various other groups of animals, some with many representatives, some with few, also contribute to the complex of organisms living in fresh water. The word 'worm' is still commonly used, but nowadays it has lost its specific meaning in zoology, and is applied to a confusing variety of organisms. Amongst these are the planarians and the Gordiaceae, often found in our waters and sometimes introduced by accident into aquaria. Various species of planarians (*Planaria gonocephala*, for example) are easily seen under stones in streams: they are oval, grey or black, 10 to 25 mm long and are turbularian Flatworms. In common with other Hairworms, *Gordius aquaticus* is filiform (hair-like); it can grow to over a metre in length and is often found entangled with others of its kind. All worms which belong to the large group Annelida (of which the

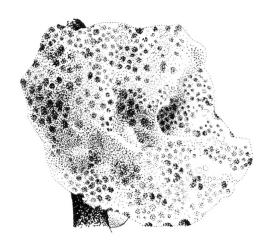

Earthworm is typical) have segmented bodies, or – to use the scientific term – they are metameric. All freshwater species are hermaphrodite. *Tubifex tubifex* (40 mm) is red; it is often found in great numbers, half buried in the mud and disappearing completely at the slightest alarm. Very similar and with the same habits is *Lumbriculus variegatus*, which is red or brown and very delicate. It is commonly found in mud or among aquatic plants. These small creatures are an excellent food for fishes and are often fed to aquarium specimens.

Leeches are worms endowed with a sucker at each end of the body, which they use to attach themselves to an animal from which they suck blood. The eggs are contained in small cocoons. *Hirudo medicinalis*, with varying colours, is one of the biggest species, reaching a length of 15 cm. The young are parasites of fishes and amphibians; the adults attach themselves to warm-blooded vertebrates: this is, in fact, the Leech species which was used in medical practice for bleeding.

As they are essentially marine animals the invertebrates belonging to Coelenterata (Jellyfishes, Corals, Sea Anemones etc.) and Porifera (Sponges) will be discussed in the next chapter. There are, however, a few species found in fresh waters and worth mentioning for the sake of completeness. The Hydra – from which the Hydrozoa take their name – are small cylindrical organisms, grey or green. The mouth is at one end of the body and serves also as the anal opening; it is surrounded by six or more long, thin tentacles. The other end is the base used as a means of attaching itself to aquatic plants; it can move by alternately attaching its tentacles and drawing its body forward. These organisms are very voracious catching small prey in their tentacles, on which are a small number of stinging cells. Hydra are minute (only a few millimetres in length) and must be examined with a magnifying glass. *Hydra vulgaris* is one of the most common European species. A small jellyfish, *Craspedacusta sowerbi*, with a transparent body about 20 mm in diameter, is distributed in all continents in lakes and ponds.

Freshwater sponges grow in grey or greenish jelly-like colonies either shapeless or in lobes: the skeleton is made up of hard, silica spicules. *Spongilla lacustris* and *Ephydatia fluviatilis* are the best known and, like the other species, have a very wide geographical distribution. They live in shallow streams and still water, attached to plants or stones.

Left: Freshwater sponge.
Right: The Swan Mussel (*Anodonta cygnaea*), a common freshwater bivalve.

173

Marine Invertebrates

In the study of marine animals—apart from fishes and other vertebrates—a vast and fascinating world is discovered. The ever-growing interest of amateurs, as well as scientists, in the vast range of organisms living in the sea is due to the increase in the popularity of the aquarium. Many sea creatures can, in fact, be kept in small ornamental aquaria, as well as in the large public ones. Tropical species are, of course, particularly attractive. They are imported from the Red Sea, the Indian Ocean and from the Antilles, but are often difficult to keep as it is not possible to satisfy all their needs (in many cases unknown as yet) as regards food and conditions. It is easier, therefore, to keep in aquaria species originating from the Mediterranean, which can be equally interesting as specimens for study and observation. It is always very important, however, to consider the different eating habits (some animals are carnivorous, some vegetarian; some eat debris or plankton, etc.) and the marked sensitivity that they often have to variations, however small, in the physical and chemical condition of the water. To make an aquarium more attractive it is possible to place on the bottom of the tank shells, or pieces of the skeleton of madrepores, corals or gorgonians, or even calcareous algae.

Two points should be remembered however: first, that the objects must be meticulously washed and cleaned, to avoid pollution; and secondly, that they may have an effect on the other specimens in the aquarium. Tropical corals, for example, should never be put with Mediterranean fish. It is obvious that a certain fundamental knowledge of these marine creatures is a first necessity for an aquarist. The reader will find that many more illustrations have been provided in this chapter than in preceding ones dealing with fishes, since they have been kept in aquaria for a much longer time and are commonly seen and often better known.

Animals and plants have existed in the sea for over 500 million years. There is an enormous quantity of fossils to demonstrate the richness of the most ancient fauna and flora. They have undergone gradual changes—in structure and distribution—in the course of time, in response to the many evolutionary processes of the organisms, as well as to successive physical variations which have occurred on the earth's surface. All animals without an internal skeleton and a backbone are associated under the one name 'invertebrates'; they are very much more numerous, and therefore more varied, than the vertebrates.

Opposite page: Some beautiful examples of the Mediterranean fauna. Centre and top left: Two examples of *Cerianthus membranaceus*. Right: A Polychaete tube. Below: A Starfish (*Echinaster sepositus*) between two coral clumps (*Astroides calycularis*).

Halocynthia papillosa,
one of the most common
ascidians found in the
Mediterranean.

Marine species cover almost all zoological types, including, of course, the Protozoa — comprising microscopic single-celled species in which individual animals can be counted in millions.

Marine invertebrates (and in fact this can apply also to the marine fauna of all localities) have biological characteristics which are extremely varied and are therefore divided according to environment so as to form clearly definable groups. Some are benthic, i.e. they live on or near the sea-bed; they may be mobile (as, for example, many crustaceans and molluscs) or static (corals, sponges, etc.). Some are nektonic, i.e. active swimmers living at varying depths in the open sea (as, for example, the squid), and some are planktonic, i.e. they drift along carried by waves or currents. Benthos, nekton and plankton, therefore represent three basic categories indivisibly linked: it is impossible to separate them entirely (for example, sea urchins are planktonic when in the larval stage and benthic as adults); and furthermore the connections of 'food chains' are endless and continuous. The term 'plankton' is perhaps the most commonly known, as it embraces a vast complex of organisms (some microscopic in size) that is of great importance as food to fish and

other animals. The marine fauna is distributed either along the shores and therefore at shallow depths (littoral fauna), or in open seas (pelagic fauna), or at great depths (sometimes 10,000 m below sea level or more). The salt content and the temperature of the water, as well as light, are of basic importance in the life of all species: in the case of the benthos, the nature of the bottom is an additional factor. The ever-increasing spread of pollution has today created serious environmental disturbances, sometimes having disastrous effects on the inhabitants of the seas.

The members of the benthic fauna of the littoral zones are of particular interest to aquarists. Sea urchins and starfish, crabs and molluscs, corals and sponges, together with many other creatures belonging to other groups, inhabit the sea-bed of the coastal zones, living at various depths and on different types of sea-bed. The fauna, therefore, changes (and one does not need to be an expert biologist in order to realize this) according to the nature of the sea-bed and the depth. There are numerous species that like coastal rocks and linger sometimes in shallow waters and other times descend to greater depths. Molluscs, prawns, small crabs, starfish, and sponges nestle among sea-

weed or shelter in rock crevices. Wherever the conditions permit, coralline communities are established which contain multicoloured colonies of calcareous algae, corals, etc., usually distributed at a depth of about 10 m. The fauna found either among the *Posidonia* beds, or established on sand, mud or debris, is very different. Often the animals hide themselves in any 'soft bottoms' (mud or sand) either burying themselves, or digging 'nests'. Of great interest are the adaptations made by all sea-dwellers (of which only a minute proportion find their way into aquaria).

Tunicates. The 'tunic' to which the name of this animal group refers, is, in fact, a hard layer of varying thickness covering the body of these animals, made from a substance which is similar to plant cellulose. All tunicates (Sea Squirts) are aquatic and marine creatures with a very characteristic structure; the individuals often come together to form colonies. They are hermaphrodite and reach maturity through more or less complex stages of metamorphosis. There are about 2,000 known species of which about 100 are planktonic. The benthic Sea Squirts are distributed in all seas and are known by the name of ascidians. They are very common in the Mediterranean and in British waters

and various species can be observed in the aquarium to which they adapt without difficulty. The best known is probably *Ciona intestinalis*, which is similar to a fairly thin and translucent cylinder about 15 cm long. It is fixed to a base by one end, while from the other protrude two 'siphons', the longer one being used for the intake of water—and therefore food (all Sea Squirts eat minute organisms) and oxygen—and the shorter for the expulsion of waste matter, after the water has been circulated internally. This species is plentiful even in the polluted waters of docks and can breed in aquaria, where it is often present by accident, as the larvae are introduced in the sea water. Much larger is the showy *Phallusia mammillata*, which is up to 25 cm high, with a white or yellowish tunic covered in lumps either irregular or roundish in shape. It is found in large numbers on sea-beds of various kinds and, as a rule, has a short life in the aquarium. The *Halocynthia papillosa* has an attractive appearance: the body is oval and bright red; it lives on coralline beds and among *Posidonia*. The so-called Sea Lemon (*Microcosmus sulcatus*), with a brown shell which is always encrusted with various growths, is also an ascidian. It forms large colonies and it is fished

Two photographs showing the variety of colours displayed by the Feather Star (*Antedon mediterranea*).

177

The Sea Cucumber
(*Cucumaria planci*) with
the characteristic regular
series of tube-feet.

and used as food. Salps are gelatinous and planktonic tunicates that appear in great numbers in European seas, mostly in winter and spring.

Echinoderms. All members of this group live in the sea. There are about 6,000 living species known, to which may be added an even larger number of fossils. The members of the group greatly differ in shape, colour and mode of life; their strange forms and bright colours make the echinoderms some of the most beautiful creatures of the underwater world. Contrary to what the name implies, some do not have a 'spinous skin'. All of them, however, are benthic and live on the bottom as adults, but at the larval stage, when they are very small and strangely shaped, they are planktonic; the metamorphosis is very complicated. These creatures extend from the edge of the sea right down to the abyssal depths of the ocean. Three morphological features are readily visible. First, in the majority of cases they have a radial symmetry to their bodies, with parts radiating from the centre, at which is placed the mouth. Secondly, they have a more or less developed horny covering, formed by little calcareous plates generally bearing spines or granules. Lastly, they have small but very mobile tentacles that are called pedicels, or tube-feet,

placed mostly along the radial lines, and used for locomotion. There are five well-defined classes of echinoderm.

The first (crinoids) includes the sea lilies, such as the well-known *Antedon mediterranea*, commonly found around Italy. The body is small and conical in shape; it has fine tentacles that enable it to cling to algae; there are ten (five, to be exact, which are forked at the base) long flexible arms, which, in turn, bear tentacles, and give it a feathery look; these arms are extremely fragile. It is usually red, orange or yellow in colour. This pretty creature does well in the aquarium. In the tropics, mainly in Indonesian and Australian seas, can be seen some larger multicoloured species, that resemble beautiful flowers. The Sea Cucumbers or Holothurians, are the least attractive echinoderms, so much so that it is at first rather difficult to see any resemblance between them and the sea-urchins and starfishes. The body is cylindrical with the mouth at one end and the anus at the other. The mouth has a crown of tentacles around it, varying in shape and length. The protective calcareous plates are invisible, as they are microscopic and situated in great numbers in the thickness of the skin. The skin itself can be rather rough. The tubefeet are sparse

but arranged in longitudinal rows. The holothurians can easily contract, and often, if they are disturbed or alarmed, they expel viscera, which are subsequently regenerated. These animals live on different kinds of sea-beds and adapt quite well to the aquarium, but are rather uninteresting. *Holothuria tubulosa* is commonly found in the Mediterranean; it is 30 cm in length, brown, and lives on various types of sea-bed, down to a depth of 100 m. Another common species is *Cucumaria planci*, which is smaller (15 cm) with longer tentacles around the mouth.

The name Starfish or Sea Star is universally applied to the whole class of asteroids, and is fully justified by the appearance of these creatures. They have a more or less flattened body with the underside resting on the bottom and the upper part bearing a more vivid coloration. The mouth is at the centre of the underside; the arms have either two or four rows of tubefeet, often endowed with a sucker at the end, which gives them secure anchorage. Starfishes are voracious carnivores and eat a quantity of molluscs. They are easily kept in aquaria where they attach themselves to the sides. The Mediterranean species differ in size, colour and shape. The arms (that may be more than five) are

at times so short that the body becomes pentagonal. Starfishes belonging to the genus *Astropecten* are easily identified by their flat body; they have five regular arms with clearly visible marginal spined plates. They live on muddy or sandy bottoms, devouring molluscs. *A. aurantiacus* is one of the largest species, sometimes more than 50 cm in diameter. It is very common and a light reddish-brown colour, tending to orange or greyish purple. Even larger is *Luidia ciliaris* (60 cm), with seven very fragile arms, red or pinkish in colour. Sea urchins often fall prey to this species. *Asterina gibbosa* is one of the smaller species; the diameter is never more than 4 cm. The arms are very short and the body is covered by short spines. The greenish-grey colour matches the stones on which it usually rests at the bottom of the water. It is very euryhaline and many individuals are hermaphrodite. Equally common is *Echinaster sepositus* which is about 30 cm in diameter and has tubular arms, with very short spines. This beautiful sea star, which is coloured a vivid red, is found among rocks, and in *Posidonia* beds etc.

Marthasterias glacialis is one of the most common Mediterranean starfishes. It has strong spines along the arms, and a diameter of over 50 cm at

Left: A Starfish (*Echinaster sepositus*) with a regular five-point formation. Right: A view of the underside showing the mouth at the centre of the small Cushion Star (*Asterina gibbosa*).

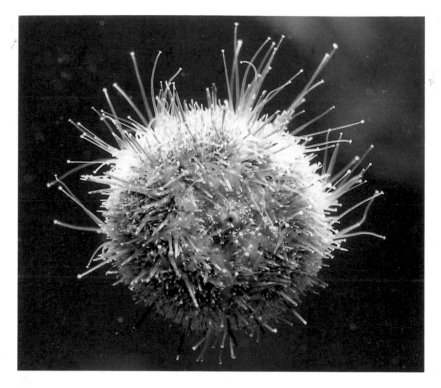

times. The colour is either green or reddish in those species living in shallower waters, and yellow or pinkish in those at a depth of about 10 m. This starfish is commonly found in various environments (rocks, etc.) and feeds on molluscs which it digests by inverting its stomach and forcing it into the shell. *Coscinasterias tenuispina*, which is light brown with darker spots, is much smaller. It has 6 to 9 arms, unequal in length. It reproduces itself by simple division of the body, especially when young. All the echinoderms so far mentioned are also found in the eastern Atlantic. In the northern European seas are found the Sun Star (*Crossaster papposa*), with 8 to 13 arms covered in bunches of short spines, and the Common Starfish (*Asteria rubens*) which has a regular formation of five rays. Amongst the eye-catching tropical species — sometimes kept in large aquaria — should be mentioned *Oreaster reticulatus* (from the Antilles) and the beautiful *Protoreaster lincki* from the Indian Ocean.

Not all the numerous members of the echinoids are classed as sea urchins. This name only applies to the ones having a spherical body covered with minute plates bearing movable spines. The mouth is placed in the centre of the underside, with five teeth radiating

from it, set in a singular and complex jaw (Aristotle's lantern). The anal aperture is placed at the opposite pole. Some thin and very mobile tubefeet protrude from amongst the dense sharp spines. Sea urchins — often kept in aquaria — are very sedentary and live on different types of sea-bed: they have larvae of an unusual shape. The eggs of some species are edible.

Stylocidaris affinis differs from the ordinary sea urchins in having much longer and stouter spines. It is found between 30 and 1,000 m in depth and is carnivorous. Two well-known species, found in large numbers on rocks and also close to the shore, are *Arbacia lixula*, with black spines, and *Paracentrotus lividus*, which has either purple, brown or greenish spines. The smaller *Psammechinus microtuberculatus*, green in colour, is often numerous in *Posidonia* beds. Two rather attractive and larger species that usually live at greater depths are *Sphaerechinus granularis* and *Echinus acutus*. The first (12 cm in diameter) has purple-coloured spines with white points and is found fairly deep down on reefs. The second is red or pinkish, with a more or less conical body and a diameter of 10 to 15 cm; it prefers living in mud at depths of between 20 m and 1,000 m and even more. Once again, it is in tropical seas that

the most handsome species of echinoid are found, such as the large *Heterocentrotus*, known for their elliptical bodies and thick cylindrical spines. Sharing the coral reefs with *Heterocentrotus* are *Echinometra*, also elliptical in shape, and *Diadema*, feared for its long, thin and rather fragile, black spines. These sea urchins have various species distributed throughout all the oceans; *Heterocentrotus*, however, is not found in the Atlantic.

The ophiuroids are a family of usually modest (sometimes even small) echinoderms, also called Brittlestars. They have five arms radiating from the body, which can be round or pentagonal, and are very thin and flexible. These species are more active than the sea urchins and the true starfishes. The flattened body allows them to hide in crevices and small recesses. Brittlestars live in dense colonies at the bottom of the sea, and they play a large part in the general marine economy. They feed on small invertebrates or swallow mud containing digestible debris. In aquaria, pieces of fish can be given as food. There are many easily identified species along the Italian coast.

Ophiothrix fragilis lives up to its name as the arms — with many lateral prickles and variously coloured (green, blue,

Left: *Ophithrix fragilis*; this creature fully justifies the name of Brittlestar.
Right: *Ophiura texturata*, that has very short spines along the arms.

Opposite page: Top left: *Psammechinus microtuberculatus* clearly showing the long mobile tube-feet.
Right: Two very common examples of sea urchins found along the Mediterranean coastal banks: *Poracentrotus lividus* (on the left) and *Arbacia lixula* (on the right).
Bottom: Juvenile *Sphaerechinus granularis*.

red, etc., with or without darker rings) — break very easily. *Ophioderma longicaudum* (brown-black, with arms up to 5 cm long) is bigger and stronger and like the previous species lives amongst the rocks or stones or the *Posidonia* at the bottom of the sea. On muddy sand, at certain depths, another large brittlestar is plentiful: *Ophiura texturata*, which is light brown or orange. Some large species have a distinctive and strange appearance: they have long arms bearing many branches that are folded inwards like a bush. Some of these are represented in the Mediterranean, such as *Astrospartus mediterraneus* — grey with a diameter reaching 40 cm — which lives at moderate depths of not less than 50 m.

Crustaceans. Some general details have already been given with regard to freshwater crustaceans. They belong to the enormous group of arthropod animals as they have articulated limbs, and they are as numerous in the sea as insects are on land. Their species are present in all environments and are both incredibly numerous and varied in form and habits. Some minute crustaceans contribute greatly to the composition of plankton, and form an important link in the food chain, while others are benthic and live not only on the different sorts of

coastal sea-beds but also in the depths of the oceans. The littoral crustaceans are obviously of more interest to us, and these include species which have economic value as food, as well as the species which are kept in aquaria where it is easy to reproduce suitable conditions for them. These, of course, are the larger and better known decapods, such as crabs and prawns. The name of this group refers to the five pairs of walking legs, placed on the front part of the body, or cephalothorax, with the foremost pair normally ending in pincer claws called chelae. Other jointed appendices are also present and this produces a complicated terminology. Those most visible beside the mouth move all the time; the eyes are carried on stalks, and the antennae — generally long and thin — are in two pairs. The rear part of the body, or abdomen, is clearly divided into successive segments. The whole animal is covered and protected by a thick calcareous armour often with spines or tubercles, which can be periodically renewed (as in freshwater crustaceans). Decapods can either walk or swim: the diet is either carnivorous or omnivorous.

The shape of a crab is unmistakable: the abdomen is reduced to a thin plate folded under the cephalothorax, which

varies in shape. In aquaria it often behaves as an aggressive predator, even eating fishes, and for this reason keeping it with other animals must be carefully considered. It is best to keep big crabs in separate tanks. *Pachygrapsus marmoratus* is very common in Mediterranean coastal waters; it has brown, yellow and greenish speckles, and a quadrangular cephalothorax. It often wanders on the shores, but is always ready to disappear into the cracks of rocks. *Eriphia verrucosa* has much the same habits but is larger than the preceding species, with larger claws and a rougher skin; it is brown with light and dark speckles. Of very different appearance is *Maja verrucosa*: it has a subtriangular body with large spines on the sides, often covered in algae which gives it a very effective camouflage. Another related species is *Maja squinado*, a little larger (20 cm) and red in colour (instead of grey), which lives lower down among debris or in mud. The Sponge Crab (*Dromia vulgarix*) and *Calappa granulata* are two strange-looking species that live further out at sea. Both have a rounded body and shortened legs: the first is dark brown and usually carries a sponge on its back (hence the name); the second is off-white with roundish red showy lumps all over, that are reminiscent of pomegranate seeds.

This species usually likes to bury itself in sand and therefore is often hidden from sight in aquaria. The so-called Spider Crabs which are species of the genus *Macropodia*, with long and slender limbs, are very common among *Posidonia* and algae. Typical inhabitants of soft bottoms (mud, detritus) are the Shore Crab (*Carcinus maenas*) – which is euryhaline and can tolerate even polluted waters, and species of *Macropipus*. They swim very well, using the last pair of legs which end with oval flat sections, and also bury themselves in sand or mud. Much more attractive are some brightly coloured crabs from tropical seas. One of these, the Fiddler Crab (*Uca*) is numerous along the coasts. The male individuals have one claw much larger than the other and they move it up and down – rather resembling a fiddler playing the violin – while standing outside their hideouts. Also to be found are members of the genus *Ocypoda* which are whitish and run swiftly across the sand.

Many other decapods have a well-developed abdomen which extends behind the cephalothorax, at the end of which – as in crayfish – there is a fan-shaped extension to the tail. The Crawfish (*Palinurus elephas*), which reaches 50 cm in length, is one of the largest decapods and is also one of

Left: *Macropodia longipes*, a Spider Crab, resembles a spider with its long legs. Right: The strange *Calappa granulata*.

Left: *Homola barbata*.
Right: The Sponge Crab (*Dromia vulgaris*) in the process of shedding its shell.

Opposite page: Top: A male Fiddler Crab (*Uca*) showing the characteristic asymmetric chelae.
Below: A species of tropical crab with an elegant coloration.

the most famous of marine animals. It does not have pincers and the prevalent colours are red, yellow and brown. It lives on rocky bottoms, between depths of 15 and 100 m. It settles well in aquaria where it can be fed dead fishes and small molluscs. Larger than the Crawfish is the Lobster (*Homarus gammarus*), which attains 60 cm; the pincers are very large and the whole body is covered in light blue and yellow stripes. This crustacean lives at considerable depths crawling along rocky shores. A decapod that is widely known for its food value — but not often seen in aquaria — is the Norway Lobster (*Nephrops norvegicus*) or Scampi. It is smaller than the ones previously described, whitish with red patterns and spots. It crawls on mud at depths of between 30 and 800 m.

The Crawfish, Lobster and Scampi all have long, thin antennae, while *Scyllarus arctus* has short broad feelers, laminated and hairy around the edges. It measures about 12 cm; it is dark brown with red spots on the abdomen. It lives on rocks and in *Posidonia*. There are many species of prawns such as the small *Palaemon*, which is commonly found among stones in small rock pools, along the shores, or the pretty *Lysmata seticaudata*, with characteristic long fine antennae of a delicate pink, and with red lengthwise

stripes. The Imperial Prawn (*Penaeus kerathurus*) is bigger — reaching 20 cm — and orange in colour; it crawls on mud or sand and is also one of the most edible species.

There is a series of decapods that differ from those already described in some fundamental characteristics, such as major or minor reduction in the size of the rear legs. The Squat Lobster (*Galathea strigosa*), measuring 6 cm, has, in fact, the fifth pair of legs much foreshortened; the pincers are long and thorny. This crustacean is red with blue lines across the body and is found down to a depth of about 100 m. The Hermit Crabs are very well known. They have three main distinguishing features: the pincers are asymmetrical (one is smaller than the others); the fourth and fifth pair of legs are very short and the abdomen is soft. This part of the body is, in fact, spirally coiled to fit shells of gasteropod molluscs, in which it finds shelter. All Hermit Crabs crawl about on the bottom of the sea, carrying their home which they change periodically, as they develop, and into which they quickly withdraw when in danger. Often sponges or sea-anemones encrust the shell, and this gives one of the best-known examples of animal symbiosis. Hermit Crabs devour debris and in aquaria are most

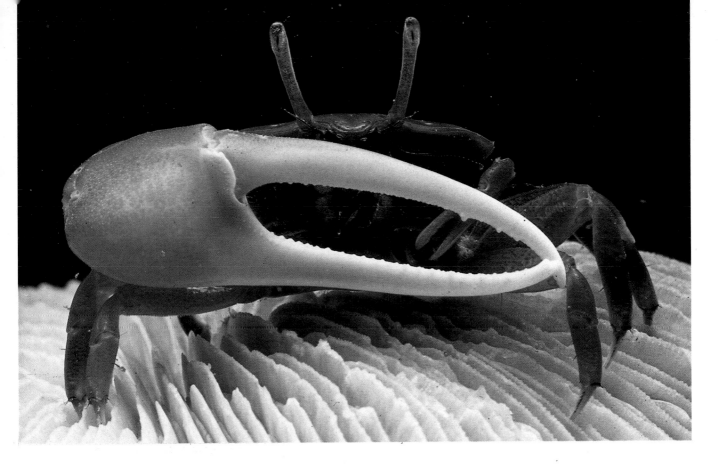

Top: An example of Common Lobster (*Homarus gammarus*), a large crustacean having powerful pincers. Below: Crawfish (*Palinurus vulgaris*).

useful for keeping the bottom free of dirt. *Dardanus arrosor*, red in colour, is the most common Mediterranean species and is popular in aquaria.

There is yet another order, the stomatopods which contains the species Mantis Prawn (*Squilla mantis*) sometimes also called Mantis Shrimp. Six walking limbs are used for propulsion, while in front is an enlarged pair adapted into huge traps which swing shut over the prey, similar to the forearms of the Praying Mantis. The Mantis Shrimp attains a length of 25 cm and is light yellow in colour. It is found on mud or sandbanks to a depth of 100 m. There are a few other species of crustaceans worth mentioning, even though they are not considered to be 'aquarium specimens' The amphipods, for example, include the various small species of sand fleas or beach hoppers which make a good diet for fishes. They have limbs adapted for hopping and a body which is laterally compressed. The isopods, on the other hand, are broad and compressed dorso-ventrally. Of these the cimothoids are of particular interest for they attach themselves to fishes as external parasites and also enter the mouth and gill chamber from which they suck blood. *Nerocila bivittata* (easily identified by the two yellow stripes along its back) can

often be seen attached to Wrasses or Sea Breams etc.

The Acorn Barnacle (*Balanus*) is the best known cirripede. It has a conical chalky shell, by means of which it clings to rocks along the shore, protruding from it with numerous curved limbs. Blennies are particularly fond of barnacles. Turtles can often be seen carrying their own parasite, the whitish, flat Turtle Barnacle (*Chelonobia testudinaria*). The crab parasite, *Sacculina*, is very untypical of its class, but is also a cirripede. It attaches itself to the underside of a crab and looks like a fleshy excrescence without a hard shell. Other strange fish parasites are the many kinds of copepods, such as *Peroderma, Caligus*, etc., which do not share the characteristics of their mainly planktonic relatives. They appear as a very soft tumour-like swelling adapting their parasitical life-style to the body of their host.

Molluscs. There is a fundamental difference between crustaceans and molluscs which is readily apparent to an observer: molluscs do not have a hard covering or articulated limbs. The name mollusc was given to these creatures a long time ago by ancient scholars and is extremely apt as their body is, in fact, very soft and has fleshy tentacles. The shell which protects many molluscs is mainly formed of calcium carbonate within a mantle, or fold of skin, by which it is secreted. The shells of molluscs are enormously varied in shape, colour and dimension according to species. For this reason, sea shells are attractive in many ways and to a vast number of people. They interest naturalists and other scientists and are much sought after by collectors. They can also be artistically arranged at the bottom of the aquarium, where they look ornamental and, at the same time, provide a shelter or a resting place for hiding organisms. As already mentioned with regard to the freshwater fauna, some molluscs are suitable for aquaria, whereas some species simply bury their way into the sand where they remain hidden.

The molluscs have one of the largest number of species amongst all types of animals and they are mostly aquatic. In the sea are found the greatest variety and number. They are divided into three main classes: gasteropods (whelks, cowries, cones) in which the shell (if present) is made in one piece and generally twisted into a spiral formation; lamellibranchs (mussels, oysters, etc.) which always possess double shells; and cephalopods (cuttlefish, octopus etc.) which very rarely have shells. The

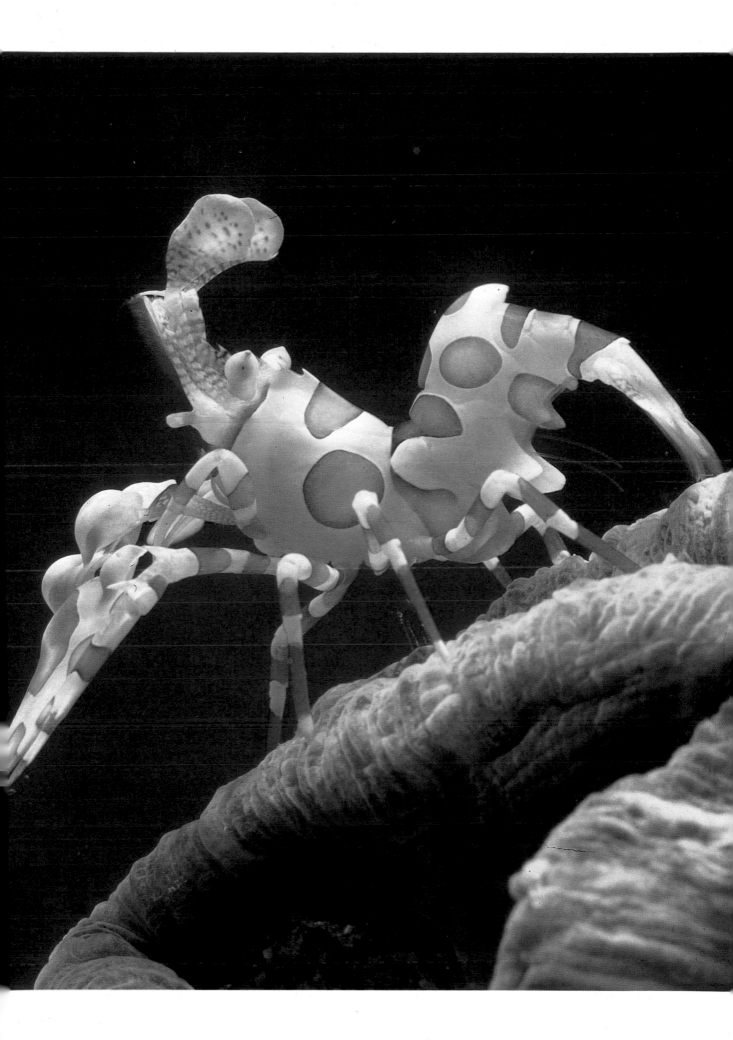

Right: Hermit Crab (*Dardanus arrosor*) with a sea anemone (*Calliactis parasitica*) attached to its shell.
Below: Another example of symbiosis: *Pagurus prideauxi* living with *Adamsia palliata*, that is seen here with extended stinging filament.

largest class is the gasteropods. The marine species — found in many different environments — breathe through gills and have a foot or small flat contractile ventral foot which enables them to crawl about on the sea-bed. Some of them have shells without a spiral. The shell of the Limpet (*Patella coerulea*), 3 to 4 cm long and grey on the outside with a blue iridescent shiny inside, is in fact shaped as a short cone. This well-known mollusc clings obstinately to rocks and stones: in the aquarium it clings to the glass and the foot is then clearly visible. In the Sea-ear or Ormer (*Haliotis striata*) the shell, measuring 7 to 8 cm, has a very small spiral, surrounded by a flat large base with series of aligned holes: the inside of the shell is iridescent. This animal is very common along the Mediterranean coastline. Some much larger, related species are found in other seas; for example, around California where they are highly valued as food and are called Abalone. Many gasteropods live together on the rocks of the seashores and are often seen amongst the seaweed or on bare stones. *Trochochlea turbinata* has a shell in a fat cone shape; it is grey with black spots, and no longer than about 2 cm. Small hermit crabs often adopt these shells when empty for their use.

Left: Squat Lobster
(*Galathea strigosa*).
Below: A large gasteropod
mollusc sliding along the
sea-bed.

Rock whelks, which crawl about on stones at various depths, are bigger and their shells are creased and spiny. They are valued as food, but their greatest fame was due to the Imperial purple, a purplish-red dye that in the past was extracted from the body of these molluscs and used for dyeing cloth. The eggs are often found on beaches, laid in little clusters contained in a parchment-like casing. *Murex brandaris* has a yellowish or grey shell which attains a length of about 9 cm and is covered with sharp spines; while *M. trunculus* is slightly bigger with a smooth shell.

Cassidaria echinophora is another common gasteropod in the Mediterranean and lives at depths between 25 and 100 m: it has an oval shell (8 cm long), light brown in colour and covered by white tubercles. *Dolium galea* is much larger (25 cm) and has a similar vertical distribution as the last species but it is less frequent; it is found on muddy bottoms, and among debris. The shell is more or less spherical, with numerous parallel grooves and a large opening. It is a voracious predator and kills other molluscs with its saliva which contains sulphuric acid. The largest Mediterranean gasteropod is *Charonia nodifera*: the shell is shaped in a high pointed spiral (it grows to

30 cm in height), is rather thick, and speckled in brown, yellow and red on a yellowish-white background. In the past the empty shell was used as a horn by removing the apex.

Both the size (which at times can be considerable) and the difficulty in capturing the very colourful and attractive species living in tropical waters, often prevent them from being kept in the aquarium. The most eye-catching species are perhaps the cowries, such as the Tiger Cowrie (*Cyprae tigris*), a species commonly found from the Red Sea to the Pacific. As with related species this mollusc is omnivorous. When the animal is alive, the large lobes at the sides of the 'mantle' almost cover the whole shell. The shell is oval and shiny, speckled in brown and up to 10 cm long. There are only very few representatives of this family living in the Mediterranean; one of them is *Talparia lurida* (3 cm), which has a rather attractive brown shell, with two black spots at each end. The name *Conus* is self-explanatory with regard to the shape of the several species belonging to this family such as *C. litteratus*, *C. geographus*, etc.) which live in the warm zones of all the oceans. They are carnivorous and have a venomous sting, which is used to kill their prey. The venom in the sting of larger

Top left: *Natica millepunctata.*
Right: *Cyprea lurida.*
Below: *Cyprea tigris* lives in the Red Sea and the Indian Ocean and is perhaps one of the best known cowries.

Top left: An example of genus *Aplysia*, a mollusc that devours algae.
Right: A small gasteropod of the genus *Simia* that lives on gorgonians.
Below: *Peltodoris atromaculata*, a nudibranch mollusc common in the Mediterranean.

Opposite page: Top left: *Glossodoris valenciennesi* (the tufted gill formation is clearly visible).
Right: A small species of cephalopod with ten tentacles similar to squids.
Below: A Scallop (*Pecten jacobeaus*): the shell of this species is very well known.

Conus species can also cause very severe pain in humans and it is therefore necessary to handle these molluscs with care. One small species, *C. mediterraneus* — with a greenish-grey shell, about 2 cm long — is found along the Mediterranean shores. Again, the tropical genus *Cassis*, has a Mediterranean representative called *C. saburon*, which has a roundish light-brown shell (about 10 cm long), with numerous parallel grooves running along the spiral.

Among the most typical species of Caribbean fauna is *Strombus gigas*. It is a large mollusc actively fished both because it is edible and because of its massive shell (30 cm long) which is sold to tourists as a souvenir. The shell is thick, whitish on the outside and pink inside. The Sea Hare (*Aplysia punctata*) is very commonly found on rocks and stones in the Mediterranean coastal zones. It resembles a large snail and is dark brown in colour with two pairs of tentacles on the head and lobes spreading out from each side of the body large enough to cover the rudimentary shell which is almost invisible externally. The Sea Hare does well in the aquarium; it is strictly vegetarian and can be fed on algae (such as sea lettuce or *Ulva*). Large numbers of eggs are laid during the

Top: Cuttlefish (*Sepia officinalis*), one of the best known cephalopods.
Below: The Giant Clam (*Tridacna*), the biggest bivalve mollusc. It is found in tropical seas.

summer in thin jelly-like tubes which are attached to stones.

The nudibranchs have gills which are clearly visible on the outside of the body, and no shells. They are small and slug-like in shape with numerous brightly coloured surrounding filaments. They can only be kept in an aquarium for a few days at the most, because they are very delicate and have a highly specialized diet. Two species often found among algae are *Glossodoris gracilis* (10 cm), blue with yellow lines, and *Flabellina affinis* (15 mm) which is pink. *Peltodoris atromaculata* (50 mm), which is white, with large brown-black patches, lives on *Petrosia* sponges.

The lamellibranchs are the second most numerous class of molluscs. They are easily recognizable by their shell (which is in two parts), the absence of a properly developed head, and the lamellate gills. The 'seafood' species (oysters, mussels, cockles, etc.) are static inhabitants of the benthos and not very attractive for the aquarium. The scallops, on the other hand, are much more interesting: the large *Pecten jacobaeus*, for example, with its well-known shell 10 to 12 cm in diameter, is cream or white with one valve convex (the right-hand one, at the bottom) and the other flat. This mollusc, and some

similar, smaller species, is very common in the Mediterranean and can perform some eye-catching jumps springing up from the sea-bed with strong flapping movements of the valves, moving along in the water with a zig-zag movement and falling again, some distance away. The *Lima hians*, also very active, is found mainly among *Posidonia* beds. It has an oblong white shell with ridges radiating with the apex, and several red filamentous tentacles, hanging outside the shell. *Avicula hirundo*, on the other hand, is constantly attached to gorgonians; it has a brown shell of irregular shape. The Fan Shell (*Pinna nobilis*), which can grow to a length of 60 cm, is the biggest bivalve living in the Mediterranean Sea, and is sometimes kept in large aquaria. It usually attaches the apex of its triangular shell — which is reddish white and thickly covered with scale — to the sea-bed.

The cephalopods have an extremely characteristic form. The body is shaped like a sack; the head is very large and has several tentacles with a series of suckers running along inside each of them; the mouth is situated at the base of the tentacles and has a strong horny back. All these molluscs are marine, and the only one among them which has a well-developed shell is

Left: Octopus (*Octopus vulgaris*).
Right: Smaller Octopus (*Fledone cirrosa*). Both are seen in the swimming position.

197

Nautilus pompilius of the Indo-Pacific. There are many species of cephalopods can change colour in a matter of seconds, due to numerous chroaquarium specimens. The Cuttlefish (*Saepia officinalis*) is endowed with eight short tentacles, plus two much longer ones, which can be extended very rapidly when capturing a prey. The body is oval with a (fin) extension running all round its edge. All cephalopods can changes colour in a matter of seconds, due to numerous chromatophones (colour cells) within the skin. The true Squid (*Loligo vulgaris*) is bigger than the Cuttlefish (50 cm as against 25 cm) but unlike the latter it does not live long in an aquarium. It has the same number of tentacles with a more elongated body which is white, with red and brown spots. The Octopus (*Octopus vulgaris*) differs from the two species just mentioned, in that it has eight tentacles in all, and has a roundish body. It lives among coastal rocks and quickly hides in crevices when prey, generally crustaceans, approach, ready to attack. It can be kept in the aquarium, where it breeds. The eggs are laid in little bunches and protected by a jelly-like substance. They are attached to rocks and are guarded by the female. The Octopus is known to have attained a maximum of 3 m in length,

while the smaller species, *Eledone moschata* — living at greater depths on mud-banks — does not grow beyond 30 cm. This species also has eight tentacles, but each of them only bears one row of suckers (not two or three as in the Octopus).

Cnidaria. The small *Hydra* sometimes attached to vegetation in ponds (see previous chapter) are the classic example of this type of organism, which is almost entirely marine. Whether single or in vast colonies, attached to the sea-bed or floating freely in the water, they never fail to arouse admiration for the beauty of their form and their delicate coloration. Many of them are jelly-like and transparent. The symmetric structure of their body is emphasized by the tentacles surrounding the mouth, which, in fact serves both for digestion and circulation, and is also called 'coelenteron' (hence the other name for these animals: Coelenterata). Contact with these creatures can cause great irritation of the skin as they have stings or thread cells (nematocysts) all over their body and particularly on their tentacles, which are used for catching and killing prey; they are all carnivorous. Although relatively few species can be kept in aquaria, those that can are interesting: and some make beautiful ornaments.

The Greek word 'anthos' (flower) provides an appropriate name for the Anthozoa which include sea anemones and actinians. The body of these animals is soft, cylindrical or conical and contractile. It attaches itself to the sea-bed, with the base, while the top part has numerous tentacles prettily arranged in a crown like the petals of a flower; these are deceptive, however, for, as a victim approaches, the tentacles (that are usually drawn in) unfold quickly to catch the prey and bring it to the mouth which is situated at the centre of the tentacles. *Actinia equina*, 4 to 8 cm high, and bright red in colour, is very commonly found in shallow waters, attached to rocks along the Mediterranean coast. In bright sunshine it withdraws its tentacles completely and its appearance justifies in full the common name of 'Strawberry Anemone' given locally to it. It can easily be kept in an aquarium, where it does well and lives for a long time. *Anemonia sulcata* is much larger. This species has long whitish tentacles, with pink and purple tips, which can often be seen moving on rocks and stones along shallow beaches. *Condylactis aurantiaca* has shorter tentacles and is an orange colour, with white vertical stripes: it is usually found half hidden in sand in shallow waters.

Calliactis parasitica is brown with vertical stripes which range from cream to white; it has short tentacles. This species, which is about 10 cm high, is commonly found at a depth of about 20 to 100 m. It usually forms a symbiosis with the Hermit Crab which lives in the same shell on which can be found 3 to 4 anemones, as well. The *Calliactis* has the habit of extending some long and thin white filaments called 'aconthiae' from its side, if it is irritated. Some large tropical anemones are imported into Europe as aquarium specimens (as, for example, *Discosoma*, *Stoichactis*, etc.) and they can grow up to a metre in diameter. They also form symbiosis with small fishes of the family Pomacentridae (as we have already seen in a previous chapter). These animals are very difficult to keep in aquaria, because, quite apart from their large size, they need constantly flowing water and a very strong light, due to some microscopic algae (Zooxanthellae) living all over the body, which are important to their metabolism.

Cerianthus membranaceus, though similar to the sea anemones in appearance, is in fact quite different. It is a creature of great beauty and is often one of the most attractive specimens in an aquarium, where it

Top left: *Condylactis aurantiaca*, similar to an underwater flower.
Top right: A pretty Sea Anemone of the genus *Bunodactis*.
Below: Snakelocks Anemone (*Anemonia sulcata*), very common along the Mediterranean shores.

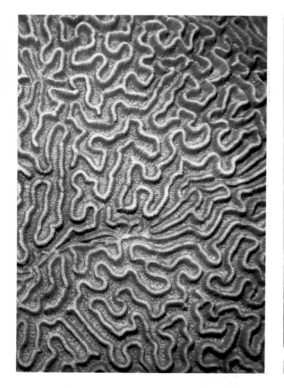

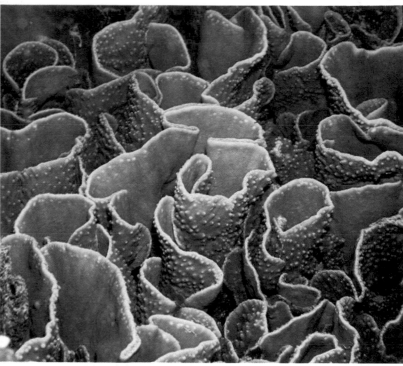

Top left: The strange
sight of coral growth with a
grooved pattern similar
to a maze.
Right: *Turbinaria
mesentherina*, a coral with
a wavy ribbon formation.
Below. Part of a colony of
Lobophyllia, a tropical coral
with green polyps.

Right: Polyps of a solitary coral.
Below: Countless individuals (polyps) form a large colony of tropical coral.

can live as long as 30 years. This beautiful underwater 'flower' can be 25 cm high; the body is an elongated tube protected by a membrane into which it can retract. Part of it is usually embedded in mud or sand and sometimes only the tentacles are visible; these form a large, splendid crown of various colours (green, purple, brown and black).

The corals are anthozoa generally associated with tropical seas, where they grow in vast masses along the coasts and give a characteristic appearance to the underwater fauna. Corals are usually in colonies with a vast number of individuals (polyps) attached to a common calcareous skeleton that can be either ramified or branched like a bush, or have other forms. These colonies can form banks, reefs and atolls in the warmer zones. The polyps resemble small sea anemones and have retractable tentacles that are extended at night to catch food (mainly microscopic plank-tonic organisms). When the individuals are alive, the colony has varied coloration, which disappears when the soft bodies are removed. A whitish dry skeleton is then left which bears a mass of little holes showing the places where the individual polyps grew. Sometimes the polyp cavities are confluent and form sinuous canals.

A colony of corals:
Cladocora cespitosa.

A solitary coral:
Leptosammia pruvoti.

Opposite page: Top left:
An eye-catching gorgonian
or Sea Fan (*Paramuricea
clavata*).
Right: Colonies of
Parazoanthus axinellae
often cover Mediterranean
rocks.
Below: Another species
of *Parazoanthus*.

This page: The white
polyps of the red coral
(*Corallium rubrum*) make
a contrast with the
colour of the skeleton,
when they are extended
(see photograph above
right).

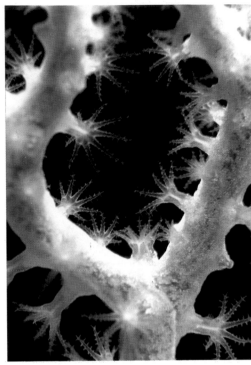

Some branches — enlarged view — of gorgonian (*Eunicella stricta*), right; and (*E. cavolini*), left. The polyps are expanded and easily visible.

Opposite page: Some photographs of colonies of species of *Alcyonium*, with polyps in the expanded and retracted position.

Some coral skeletons (such as *Acropora, Pocillopora*, etc.) make attractive ornaments for aquaria (always provided that the latter contain tropical marine specimens). Even though the Mediterranean does not have the dream-like splendour and beauty of the tropical coral beds, it includes quite a few species of Cnidaria among its marine fauna. In the warmer southern zones (such as the Gulf of Naples and along the coasts of Sicily some thick orangey masses of *Astroides calycularis* can often be seen attached to rocks at depths ranging from 1 to 50 m. Even more widely spread is the *Cladocora cespitosa*, of which colonies, 10 to 20 cm high, are brown in colour and more or less hemispherical and lightly branched with polyps growing out of the ends. It is common in various depths from a few metres down to 600 m. *Leptosammia pruvot* is a good example of non-colonial Mediterranean coral. It has bright yellow polyps, each with a cylindrical body a few centimetres long, which cover the rock like stars to a depth of a few metres (coral-bed level). *Parazoanthus axinellae* is a Zoantharia, not a coral. The yellow or orange coloured polyps are massed in colonies (often very large) and have no calcareous skeleton; they often cover

rocks or sponges, or cling to other organisms. This species is very common and contributes to the many-coloured coral of the Mediterranean. To another group (the Alcionaria) belong diverse colonial Cnidaria characterized by the fact that each polyp has eight feathery tentacles. The Common Coral (*Corallium rubrum*) looks like a little tree, and can grow to a height of over 30 cm. Its well-known red colour contrasts with the white of the open tentacles of the polyps. This is one of the most typical representatives of the Mediterranean fauna, and extends into the adjoining Atlantic as well. It grows in caves or under rocks at depths varying from about 20 to 50 m down to 200 m. The skeleton of the Coral is rigid, as it is completely calcareous, but the gorgonians (Sea Fans) have a flexible body formed by a horny central axis, which is only superficially encrusted with lime salts. The gorgonians have a very pretty miniature tree-like formation, covered in a great number of small polyps similar to little flowers. *Eunicella stricta* is whitish or greenish with almost parallel stalks growing up to 40 cm in height, and is found from depths as shallow as 6 to 7 m. *E. cavolini* is more branched and truly fan-shaped, yellow or orange. It also forms miniature

forests on the rocks, but at a slightly greater depth (coral-bed level). The skeleton of these animals is white when it is dried up, and it is pretty enough to be put into aquaria where it can create the 'marine' environment and serve as an ornament.

Paramuricea clavata is much larger (it can reach 1 metre) and stouter than the previous ones. It is purplish or violet (but turns black when dead) and is thickly branched. It is very common on rocks at depths of around 30 m. Members of the genus *Alcyonium* differ in that they are a mass of finger-shaped lobes bearing transparent polyps with calcareous particles (spicules) inside them. *A. palmatum* — 20 cm and more in height — is whitish, pink or red. It has a well-developed base, which is firmly embedded in mud. *A. acaule*, frequently found in coral beds, is red and smaller in size and usually fixed to rocks.

All the cnidarians mentioned so far are benthic, but in large aquaria it is possible to keep some planktonic species as well. However they cannot usually be kept for long. Jellyfishes are gelatinous and umbrella-shaped: some are minute, some quite large. *Pelagia noctiluca*, for instance, is one of the largest species; it is a luminescent pink colour and has an extremely irritant sting. *Rhizostoma*

pulmo — also common in the Mediterranean — is even bigger, measuring up to 60 cm in diameter. It is white with a deep blue rim. One of the smallest species is *Cladonema radiatum* (3 mm in diameter), which has a thread-like filament and usually attaches itself to *Posidonia*. Even more delicate than the true jellyfish are the Siphonophores, which are floating colonies composed of jelly-like individuals of different kinds and they can vary from being transparent and almost invisible in the water to shades of pink or blue. The By-the-wind Sailor (*Velella velella*) is frequently found as part of the Mediterranean plankton. It is prettily shaped in an elliptical thin plate, with a little sail-like crest coming out of its centre rather like a small sail in a boat.

Porifera. This name embraces all types of animals which are commonly called sponges. With few exceptions these are all marine species and very widely spread in all seas to which they contribute with their particular beauty and colours. These organisms are always attached to rocks, and have very varied forms: they may be hemi-spherical, cup-shaped, tubular, branched, or just shapeless, as when they cling to rocks, algae etc., and form large encrusted areas. They are, however, living organisms always

supported by a mineralized skeletal
framework of spicules (of either silica
or lime) or by a horny substance
thickly knitted together. Sponges are
microphagous: they feed on microscopic particles brought in the water
and drawn in through the numerous
pores scattered all over the body
(hence the name 'Porifera'). As these
creatures are completely static and
devoid of any relationship with their
surroundings, they are of little interest
to the aquarist. They can, however, be
used in an aquarium as ornaments or
as a support or shelter for other
organisms. Some common species
that are part of the Mediterranean
benthos are useful for this purpose.
Spongia officialis is the well-known
bath sponge. It has a horny skeleton;
when alive, it is black and its fleshy
body is either hemispherical or it
appears as a round cushion, sometimes more than 20 cm in diameter. It
is usually found attached to rocky
banks under the sea up to a depth of
about 50 m. Siliceous sponges are
very numerous. Several species of
Axinella are found on rocky sea-banks
at various levels. They are either fan-
shaped or tree-like, and yellow or
orange in colour. *Petrosia ficiformis* is
thick and hard and very varied in
shape and colour (usually brown or
deep purple). *Calyx nicaensis* is

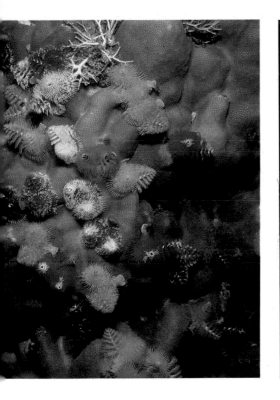

Top: Many species of
polychaete worm live
attached to the sea-bed,
in tubes from which only
a multicoloured crown
of tentacles emerges
(see top right).
Below: *Retepora cellulosa*, a
bryozoan with a delicate
lacy formation.

brown and — as the name implies — is cup-shaped; it can grow up to a height of 20 cm. All these species are very common. *Tethya aurantium* and *Suberites domuncula* are also siliceous sponges, both more or less spherical in shape, and orange-red in colour. The first has a lumpy surface while the second is smooth. *Suberites* is always firmly installed on shells inhabited by Hermit Crabs and can almost cover the whole shell. Often seen clinging to the sides of aquaria are small whitish or light-brown sponges which have been introduced with sea water when in their larval stage. Very often they are the *Sycon raphanus*, which grows to a maximum height of 2 cm, and has a calcareous skeleton. It is a world-wide species.

Other marine invertebrates. Bryozoans are minute marine animals, rather resembling the polyps of coelenterates, with a slightly different structure. They are also called Polyzoa. They, too, live in colonies of varied shapes covering large surfaces of rocks, stones, algae, sea shells, etc. *Retepora cellulosa* is one of the prettiest species. It looks like delicate pink crumpled lace and is calcareous but extremely brittle. It is commonly found on rocks at fairly deep levels under the sea, where *Myriapora truncata* is also found. The latter has

colonies supported by a calcareous skeleton, rather resembling corals but differing in its regular paired branching. The annelids — all of which have a regular segmented body, similar to the Earthworm — include a great number of marine species. Some of them are so beautifully formed as to make one revise the rather negative aesthetic judgment usually given to the so-called 'worms'. One of the most common Mediterranean species — often kept in aquaria as well — is *Spirographis spallanzani*, measuring about 30 cm. It lives inside a papery tubular structure, fixed upright in mud, at relatively shallow depths. From this stem-like container emerges the front part of the animal, bearing a crown of spiralling gill tentacles. When the tuft is fully open, it is a magnificent sight, but the animal promptly closes it, as soon as it senses danger. There are several more species which are smaller but equally beautiful, as for instance the Peacock Worm (*Sabella pavonina*), with multicoloured tentacles forming lighter and darker zones, set side by side; and *Protula intestinum* that is enclosed in a white twisted calcareous tube, and has a reddish gill tuft emerging at one end, which tends to fade into a pinkish shade when kept in an aquarium, because of the difference in light.

Practical Tips for Aquarists

Location of the Aquarium

The exact location of an aquarium is of importance from more than one point of view. The biological requirements of its inhabitants must be met, but at the same time the layout of the furniture and the general arrangement of the room must also be taken into account, as an aquarium is often designed to fit in a room ornamentally. All this is not always easy to achieve. Before the purchase of a tank, therefore, it is wise, first of all, to decide upon the place where it is to be put and whether or not the aquarium is going to be purely functional (e.g. for experimental use in a laboratory) or just ornamental. If the latter is the case, a tank must be chosen which fits in with the rest of the furniture and the general style of the room. A modern room will easily take a tank which has simple and sober lines, while a room which is full of antiques might require a different and more appropriate style. The modern lightweight materials available — such as perspex and other plastic substances — for frames, and either wood or marble for the supporting base, offer endless possibilities for making the aquarium an integral part of the room. If a room is yet to be built, it is worth entrusting the architect or interior decorator with the task of incorporating a full 'underwaterscape' in the design of a particular room, and build the aquarium directly in one of the walls, as a special feature.

Leaving aside the various types of tanks and their respective aesthetic value, there are some general rules that must always be remembered. The aquarium should be placed so that the animals in it can always be seen easily. The best height of the support (either a table or a chest) is about 70 cm but naturally this also depends upon the type of room. For instance, in a living room where one is likely to be sitting down, it is best to lower the height, while, if the aquarium is kept in the hall where one will look at it when standing up, it should obviously be placed higher.

It is necessary to protect the rest of the furniture from the aquarium or, to be exact, from the water used in it. Sea water, especially, can cause a lot of damage to furniture, floors and carpets, by leaving persistent marks and spots, because of its salt content. There are, in fact, various daily tasks to be carried out in the aquarium, and once a week a thorough cleaning up, too. Therefore, before starting any of these duties, care should be taken to remove the objects likely to be spoilt, or protect them by some kind of waterproof covering.

The problem of illumination also requires some attention. Many aquarium specimens are indigenous to the tropics where a great deal of light filters through the water, and for this reason they can tolerate sunlight. However, the aquarium should never be placed near a window, because the direct rays of the sun would quickly heat the water beyond the limit which the fish could survive, and even tropical specimens would soon die. On the other hand, a spell of sunlight each day is advisable, the length of time of course depending upon the size of the aquarium. The best way is to let the sunshine on the tank either during the morning for a while or during the evening.

However, natural light is not a vital necessity for the inhabitants of the aquarium. Today it is possible to have artificial illumination which contains almost all the biologically important properties of the solar spectrum, and can be used as a substitute for natural light without any harm coming to the animals.

The Tank

There is on the market today a vast range of tanks of different types and different prices.

A tank made entirely of glass, which was once very popular, is rather out of fashion because glass is never completely smooth and may have flaws or air-bubbles. Another disadvantage is the fact that it is very fragile and can easily be broken even by being shaken too hard. It has, however, some excellent uses, as a special tank, when needed either for breeding purposes or as a 'sick bay' for isolating fish that are either diseased or in need of 'quarantine' (a perspex tank is often used for this purpose, instead of a glass one).

The tank with a frame is the oldest and most widely used type. The

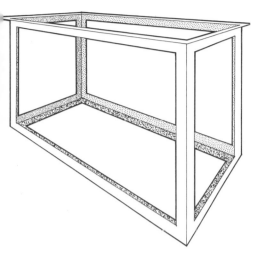

Aquarium tank with metal frame.

frame is made of either steel or another metal, to which are attached the glass walls. Metal, of course, rusts easily when in contact with water and it is therefore necessary to give it a protective coat of paint (either plastic, enamel, resinous etc.). If the frame is of stainless steel, such protection is unnecessary. The substances used on the metal must be completely free from poisonous contents, as these could be slowly dissolved by the water and constitute a threat to the fishes and other animals living in the tank.

The aquarist who intends to build a marine aquarium must take particular care, as sea water attacks metal, paint etc. even faster than fresh water, thus filling the tank with toxic substances and causing the death of fishes and invertebrates. In addition the tank itself is seriously damaged in a very short time. Therefore a marine aquarium must be completely 'sea-water' proof. The same applies to tanks with lightweight metal frames, or plastic frames and for frameless perspex tanks with bonded sides. When building a large aquarium it is best to construct the walls out of concrete with only a glass front panel. In this case it is necessary to run water through the tank for several days before using it, because fresh concrete is poisonous to fish.

There are many types of tanks available on the market nowadays, some are extremely ugly, others of excellent design and good quality. Some have a built-in recess (not visible from the front) where filters, pumps, ultra-violet lamps etc. can be unobtrusively fitted.

Thickness of glass. When buying an aquarium or building it from a 'do-it-yourself' kit, great attention should be paid to the exact thickness of the glass. Glass can easily crack if it is shaken, for example by vibration of buildings due to traffic. The thickness must be calculated in proportion to the volume of water, as this exerts a considerable pressure against the walls of the tank. For a tank one metre in length, a safe thickness would be 12 mm. It is best to use high-quality clear glass. The glass used as a base in a tank of the same measurement should be 16 mm thick; and it should be stuck with mastic so that no damp can seep through.

Another factor that must be taken into account in the making of an aquarium is its total weight. To work out the weight of water it is useful to remember that one cube of water with sides of 10 cm is equal to one litre which is one kilogram in weight. Of course the weight of the container must be added to this total, as well as that of the various other objects in the aquarium, such as stones, gravel, etc. This means that the aquarium exerts a relatively consistent pressure on one fairly limited spot, and too heavy an aquarium may cause the floor to sink or even to collapse. It is advisable therefore to consult an architect or some expert before installing a very heavy aquarium in a room.

Water

The vital element for fishes is in fact, the water; not chemically pure H_2O, but a solution of water containing various substances, such as mineral salts, air, and trace elements. In fresh water (i.e. the water obtained from taps, rivers or rain) the natural content of salts is very low. The level of minerals, salts and lime in water differs according to the locality of origin and at times water can also contain a certain amount of acid of different kinds. Water containing a high content of magnesium and chalk is called 'hard' while a low content of these salts gives 'soft' water. The degree of hardness of the water can be determined with an instrument easily obtained in a specialist shop. The instrument measures the conductivity of electricity, which is different for each type of water.

The majority of freshwater fishes live easily in water taken from taps, springs or wells. If a particularly delicate fish becomes unwell it often means that the water is polluted by some toxic substance which would be equally damaging to man's health. Some fishes need very soft water, and for them tap water should be diluted with distilled water, until it reaches the required level of softness. Other fishes like slightly salty water: in this case the right level can be obtained with the addition of some common kitchen salt or rock salt. The salinity can be checked by measuring the density of the water with the appropriate instrument. Because of widespread pollution, it is difficult nowadays to find pure water, and therefore it is best to use water from the mains or from fountains. In the past, rain water was preferred for aquaria, but now because of the high level of air pollution, caused by industry and domestic coal smoke, exhaust fumes etc. rainwater collected in or near big cities and industrial centres often contains such a high concentration of acids and other poisonous chemicals, that fishes, particularly the more delicate ones, deteriorate rapidly. The best source of water for aquaria is therefore a spring.

Sea water has a salt content varying between 2% and 4%. The saltiness is easily detected by taste. In regions where there are large outlets of fresh water into the sea, such as in large river mouths and lagoons — there is a low content of salinity and in this case we talk of brackish water.

In oceanography 'salinity' includes all the chemical compounds dissolved in the water. The average salt content of the water in the open seas is 3·5%, i.e. 35 parts per thousand. As one litre of water weighs one kilogram, this means that there are 35 g of salts in each litre: of this 88·6% are chlorides; 10·8% sulphates; 0·6% carbonates, bromides, etc.

The trace elements constitute less than 1% of the substances dissolved in the water, but they are biologically very important for various reasons. The salinity of the Atlantic and the Pacific ranges between 34 and 36 parts per thousand. In seas that are enclosed, with small inlets of fresh water, the salt content is considerably higher. The salinity of the Mediterranean is 37 parts per thousand; and that of the Red Sea is over 41 parts per thousand. On the other hand, enclosed seas with a large inflow of fresh water have a low degree of salinity: the salt content of the Black Sea is, for instance, only between 15 and 18 parts per thousand. It is useful for an aquarist to know these data, in order to avoid putting a fish belonging to the Mediterranean fauna in an aquarium suitable, say, for fishes from the Black Sea, or the other way round, which would have even worse consequences.

There are three ways of providing water for a marine aquarium:

1. Procure water directly from the sea. This procedure is costly and unrewarding. Sea-water is occasionally supplied to large public aquaria either by pumps connected directly to the sea or by tankers, but the average aquarist cannot avail himself of this facility (unless, of course, he lives by the sea), and, besides, he cannot be sure that the sea water is pure. Along the European coasts, there are often discharges of sewage and industrial waste, as well as pollution from oil tankers. One more danger is the tendency of the planktonic life present in the water to die during transportation, and turn the sea water into an evil-smelling liquid.

2. Prepare artificial sea water. Although rather old, the following prescription still has some value, according to recent oceanographic knowledge. The ingredients for each 100 litres are:

2,765·00 g NaCl = sodium chloride (unrefined kitchen salt)
692·00 g MgSO$_4$ 7H$_2$O = crystallized magnesium sulphate
551·00 g MgCl$_2$ 6H$_2$O = magnesium chloride (crystallized)
65·00 g KCl = potassium chloride
25·00 g NaHCO$_3$ = bicarbonate of soda
10·00 g NaBr = sodium bromide
5·00 g Na$_2$HPO$_4$ = sodium phosphate
1·50 g SrCl$_2$ = strontium chloride
0·01 g KI = potassium iodide

First of all, thoroughly dissolve all these salts in water. According to the original prescription, after this is done, the equivalent of 145 g of CaCl$_2$ (crystallized calcium chloride) must be dissolved separately in one litre of water, making sure that the chloride used is perfectly pure otherwise there is a risk of releasing chlorine. Water containing chlorine should be thoroughly shaken before use. About 160 to 170 g

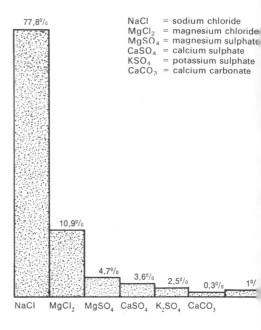

NaCl = sodium chloride
MgCl$_2$ = magnesium chloride
MgSO$_4$ = magnesium sulphate
CaSO$_4$ = calcium sulphate
KSO$_4$ = potassium sulphate
CaCO$_3$ = calcium carbonate

Percentages of salt contained in sea water.

of calcium sulphate can be used in one litre of water to be added to the main solution, instead of to the calcium chloride solution.

It must be pointed out, however, that the proportions of the quantities given in the prescription differ from the components of natural sea water. The basic elements, fluorine and boron, are absent: the percentages of sodium, potassium, magnesium, calcium, strontium, etc., are different from those contained in natural sea water and there are no trace elements. This artificial salt solution is both costly and lengthy to prepare.

Some aquarists mistakenly substitute the cheaper sodium chloride (kitchen salt) for the magnesium chloride (which is very expensive) on the principle that 'salt is salt', but this has proved to be unwise, as fishes living in this solution become weak and easily prone to diseases.

Others, equally naively, think that by using one of the many 'sea salts' easily and cheaply available on the market, they may overcome the problem of cost. This type of salt, however, comes from sea water and is not simply kitchen salt, but contains other salts as well. Since, in the extraction process normally used, sodium chloride crystallizes much more quickly than the other salts, the percentage of it in ordinary edible sea salt is much higher (more than 98%) than in the salt content of sea water.

3. Use an appropriate ready-to-use mixture of salts sold by specialized shops. This way the aquarist has no need to prepare the mixture himself or to have it prepared at a chemist's. He can buy it already made under a brand name and know that the results will generally be very good.

These mixtures normally include trace elements as well, which have a very important function in the growth of fishes, in spite of their quantity being so small in natural sea water. It is only due to their presence in the water that some vital processes can be examined and even promoted. The right dosage of trace elements is important as an overdose can be dangerous. In order to maintain the right amount frequent changes of water must be carried out: about every three weeks from one third to one half of the water in an aquarium should be changed: or one fifth every week, using artificial marine water freshly prepared from an appropriate mixture of salts plus the trace elements. At the same time the slime that usually forms at the bottom of the tank should also be removed. This routine should be observed regularly, even when the mixture does not include the trace elements. The frequency of water changes is, of course, governed by the number of fishes living in an aquarium, and this rule applies both to freshwater and sea water tanks. The pH value of the water is of paramount importance to fishes, i.e. its degree of acidity. Neutral water has a pH value of 7; water with a higher value is alkaline, a lower one acid. Freshwater fishes usually need a pH value of between about 6·5 and 7·5: even pH 8 is too alkaline for many fishes and they begin to show symptoms of illness and in the long run die of poisoning. A pH value of 9 means death for most of them and the same result occurs with acid water when the pH value is 6 or lower. However, some tropical fishes prefer slightly acid (soft) water as they come from marshy regions where the water is naturally acid, due to the high degree of organic matter derived from decomposed vegetation; this degree of acidity is an absolute necessity for the survival of the fry. The pH value is measured by using special litmus paper, or a special pH meter that can be obtained in shops. Litmus paper is put in the water of the aquarium and the colour obtained when wet is checked against a range of shades which will indicate the right value of the solution. This method can be used for determining the nature of marine water too, but it only gives approximate values, and it is advisable to use a more accurate device for this measurement, as many sea water fishes are very sensitive to changes.

Natural sea water has a pH value which ranges between 7·9 and 8·5 and is of course slightly alkaline. It is found that marine fishes keep in good condition in water around a pH of 8·2 and 8·3, in some cases even 8·6. The limits of pH tolerance are 7·5 and 9·5 but it is unwise to keep too near either extremes for too long, as this can be lethal to fishes. Marine water prepared artificially by the method described above has a pH value ranging between 7·5 and 7·7 but this is unstable and changes progressively. Many synthetic marine salt preparations incorporate a wick system which has the function of stabilizing the pH value in the water from the start: in any case this has to be checked immediately after preparing the solution and for a few days afterwards, to make sure that it is stable at pH 8·5 before putting the fishes into the water. Obviously the pH must be regularly measured and rectified whenever necessary. If it is below the required level some sodium bicarbonate (ordinary baking powder, $NaHCO_3$) or some other commercial stabilizing product can be added to the water. When the value must be lowered — which is a rarer occurrence — some acid potassium phosphate (KH_2PO_4) must be used instead.

All organic waste matters (urine, and solid waste from fishes and other aquarium inhabitants) and decomposed protein (found mostly in left-over food particles) release ammonia — a highly toxic nitrogenous compound — which is normally transformed from nitrite into nitrate by nitrifying bacteria with the loss of oxygen. The nitrate content of water is beneficial as plant fertilizer in a limited quantity, but often the amount is higher than the power of absorption of the vegetation and its excess, too, can become toxic. It is impossible to state at what level nitrate in water becomes lethal, as there are different contrasting data given by various experiments. Some aquarists have had losses with a concentration of 100 mg of nitrate for each litre of water; on the other hand, some fishes have shown a tolerance to 900 to 1,000 milligrams per litre. However, it seems that some sensitive fishes — or those recently introduced to aquaria from their natural environments — are less tolerant of high nitrate concentration. The water used for a quarantine period should therefore always be freshly prepared and should not contain nitrate. Most fishes can gradually adapt to greater nitrate content. This can be controlled with partial but regular changes of the water. With a strong pumping system connected to an efficient filter (this is best situated in the inside of the tank) the nitrate content can be kept fairly low. In marine aquaria a froth-scoop can be used to remove uneaten food from the water, before the process of decomposition takes place.

Aeration

All fishes need the oxygen contained in the water, and which they breathe through the gills. Marine fishes — especially those that come from coral-reefs — need a substantial amount of oxygen and fast-moving water. These two conditions can be satisfied by means of an energetic aerator or a powerful filter. Some species love fast-running rivers in their natural environment, and others prefer living in the strong waves along seashores or under rocks: in the aquarium these fishes spend most of their time in the middle of the artificial current. The majority of fishes, however, prefer calmer waters.

A membrane type of pump bought from a specialist shop can be used to aerate the aquarium. It is important to make sure that the pump works as efficiently and as silently as possible, noiseless ones are best. The number of pipe inlets is governed, of course, by the amount of oxygen required by the fishes: fishes belonging to the coral-reefs require several aeration inlets. Naturally the sprays are strategically placed and hidden, whenever possible, in amongst the objects that 'furnish' the tank (stones, corals, etc.). Several factors must be taken into account in the choice of a pump: the number of outlets, the dimensions of the tank, and the presence of other devices, such as purifiers, filters, etc. A membrane type of pump can, of course, serve several aquaria, provided it has sufficient power to take the load. Before buying an aeration pump, the minimum power required must be calculated, plus an additional working capacity in reserve, to prevent an eventual overload. When installing the pump it is necessary to use synthetic material for pipe-connections — both straight and T joints — and for the diffusers in the aquarium. Metal cannot be used for any part that comes in contact with the water, as it is likely to rust or corrode, thus causing the release of toxic substances into the water itself. The best diffusers are made of natural stone and synthetic materials or wood (beech or lime). Aeration is usually energetic and with small bubbles; Seahorses and Pipefishes need particularly strong aeration when they are kept in an aquarium. Fishes that inhabit coral-beds in their natural environment require a very high percentage of dissolved oxygen, which goes beyond the saturation point of the water, and far above the level provided in a normally aerated aquarium. In the immediate vicinity of a coral-reef wall, it is possible to measure 250% of dissolved oxygen in water, and in the proximity of the coast it goes down to 120 to 150%, and these values are far beyond the power of any normal aeration apparatus. Even with the help of several sprays one cannot hope to achieve more than 50% dissolved oxygen in aquarium water. Delicate fishes (such as Pomacanthidae, Chaetodontidae, Acanthuridae, Anthiidae etc.) must be kept in a separate aquarium which has an extra pump (circulation pump) operated by a centrifugal motor. This system introduces a great quantity of compressed air into the water, which increases the amount of oxygen considerably, as well as mixing the water energetically. Strong currents and lots of oxygen in water stimulate the defence mechanism against diseases and, up to a point, reduce the amount of parasites in fishes.

If the pump's air inlet is placed where there is cigarette smoke or where air is polluted by industrial gas, D.D.T. or soot etc., sooner or later the fishes in the aquarium will be affected by toxic substances. to avoid this danger, a cleansing bottle must be used. For a 200-litre tank it is sufficient to use a 4 to 5-litre bottle, about $\frac{2}{3}$ to $\frac{3}{4}$ full of pure tap water, that will be placed between the pump and the aquarium. The bottle is closed with a cork which has two holes. The water from the pump is passed into a tube which goes through one of the holes in the cork, and down into a diffuser placed at the bottom of the bottle. The impurity is thus kept in the water and the purified air goes out through another pipe which stops short of the level of the water and goes through the second hole in the cork, and into the aquarium. A necessary condition for the efficiency of this method is that the bottle top is completely airtight, and ideally it should be made of rubber so that air from the atmosphere does not seep through into the bottle. About every two months the bottle should be emptied and cleaned thoroughly and filled with fresh water. To increase the purifying action, some activated charcoal can be added or, even better, a 10% solution of bicarbonate of soda can be used instead of pure tap water.

In order to limit the growth of bacteria, the air in the aquarium can occasionally be enriched with ozone. This condensed form of oxygen has a 3-atom molecule (O_3) while the natural oxygen molecule has only two atoms (O_2); ozone is, therefore, a special form of oxygen. The ozonizer condenses oxygen into ozone and consists of a high-voltage condenser which feeds an ultra-violet lamp. The rays of the lamp bombard the oxygen contained in air and partly transform it into ozone. The ozonizer can be placed between the pump and the diffuser so that the air receives more oxygen. The ozone molecule subsequently releases active oxygen which has the power to destroy bacteria, viruses, chemical impurities, etc. The ozone acts not only as an antibiotic, but, at the same time, also as a strong oxidizing agent in many chemical reactions and stops the process of decomposition. Ozone, therefore, is of great help to aquarists, keeping the water free of bacteria. Some aquarists claim to have been able to cure diseased fishes with the use of ozone. Its excessive use, though, can be harmful: free ozone is toxic and can therefore be damaging to fishes, especially if too strong a dose is released straight into the aquarium.

There are three ways in which the aquarium water can be ozone-enriched.

1. The outlet pipe from the ozonizer can be connected directly to the tank. This can be done daily for a period of 1 to 2 hours, and care should be taken with the quantity released (5 to 10 mg/h). This procedure has a positive antibiotic action. Cloudy water full of bacteria regains its clear and clean appearance immediately. Ozone can be usefully applied to combat skin parasites, as well. Fishes in need of quarantine can be put in a tank with water treated in this way for 30 minutes 3 to 6 times a day, with 5 mg of ozonized air. The treatment should last about a week.

2. So that free ozone (which is dangerous to fishes) is not

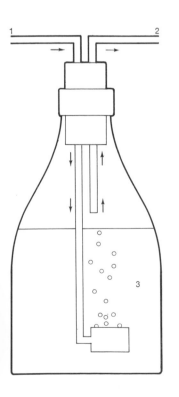

Purification bottle used for washing out the poisonous gases that may build up in an aquarium: 1, air blown in by the pump; 2, purified air, ready to return to the aquarium; 3, tap water.

223

released directly into the tank, it is best to mix ozone and air in an outside filter through a diffuser. This way the antibiotic action of the ozone can take place, while the extra quantity is dispersed by passing through the activated charcoal of the filter which will neutralize the surplus, stopping it from entering the tank. In order to achieve this, the ozone must come into immediate contact with the dirty water drawn from the tank, so that it can perform its oxidizing and antibiotic roles, while on its way to the charcoal layer. If the ozonized air comes into contact with the charcoal filter first, it will be neutralized immediately and will lose its disinfectant and antibiotic properties, before reaching the water from the tank.

3. A third method is coupling the waste-food collector with the ozonizer device. This we will discuss further on.

Let us remember that live food can also be sterilized by ozone. Tubifex and live fish can be put into an appropriate ozonizer container for at least eight hours before being fed to aquarium specimens. Ozone becomes dangerous when the water also contains ammonia and both reach a high degree of concentration; this can occur when some fishes which eat heartily expel an excessive quantity of waste. It often happens in marine aquaria after Puffer fishes have had a meal of molluscs. Some invertebrates — such as sea anemones — can be harmed or even killed by an excessive dose of ozone.

Yet again we must bear in mind that ozone causes the deterioration of vitamins. When vitamins are given to fishes, it is necessary to turn off the ozonizer for some hours. The nature of some drugs can also be altered, therefore rendered ineffective, by the oxydizing process induced by the ozone. Whenever drugs are given to aquarium inhabitants the ozonizer should be switched off until the course is completed.

Lastly it must be remembered that a large quantity of ozone is detrimental to human health, too. It is easy to detect an excess dosage of ozone by its distinctive pungent smell which will pervade the air. It can cause dizziness, headaches, general discomfort, etc.

Oxygen aeration is another expedient worth remembering. It can be achieved by passing pure oxygen through water. Thus the normal percentage of oxygen dissolved in water will be considerably increased. Large bubbles must be used in this process, as small bubbles would act directly on fishes possibly with negative results. As the oxygen dosage must not be too high, it is best to use this process only for short periods and no more than three or, at the most, four times a day, and only when necessary. A small oxygen bottle can be kept for this purpose. The oxygen treatment has similar effects to that of ozone, i.e. it can be used to help cure diseased fishes. With the introduction of a centrifuge pump, the oxygen content can be increased and controlled according to requirements.

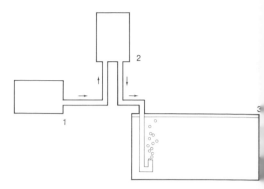

Diagram showing the connection of an ozonizer to the aquarium, permitting the intake of air that has already been enriched with ozone, before reaching the aquarium: 1, pump; 2, ozonizer; 3, aquarium. It must be remembered that this operation can lead to fishes being poisoned, if the dosage of ozone is excessive.

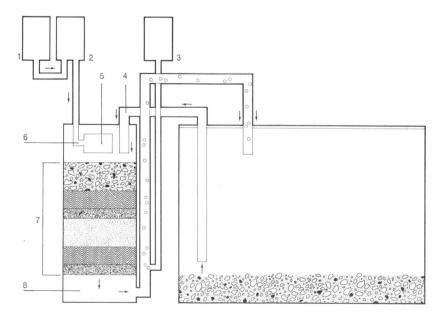

Diagram showing a method of enriching the stale water trapped in the filter with ozone, to purify it.
1, air pump for ozonizer; 2, ozonizer; 3, air pump for the filter water outlet; 4, pipe for the suction of water from the aquarium; 5, diffuser; 6, water coming from the aquarium is purified; 7, layers of different filtering materials; 8, recycling of water into the aquarium.

Filters

A filter is a must if the water is to be kept free of suspended food particles and other organic matters, and to this aim no expense should be spared. A tank can never be 'over filtered'. The following rules must be observed. A filter should always have enough power to regenerate the whole volume of water in the tank in four hours at least, though the best rate would be one hour. One important factor to take into account is the current created by the pump inside the tank. First of all, the current causes the impurities to be circulated and absorbed, and encourages the fishes to be active, greatly enhancing their welfare. It is obvious that this aim will not be achieved by a simple air pump; it is, in fact, necessary to use a centrifuge pump to obtain good results.

The best solution is offered by an external filter. A container with a filtering agent in it is placed outside the tank. This enables the collection of impurities outside the tank, and the filter can be cleaned without disturbing the aquarium inhabitants. One of the advantages of an external filter is that it generally causes a minimal heat loss in the water. It is a known fact that the water current necessary to work the filter can be generated by air. Usually the current is insufficient for a marine aquarium, and it is wiser to connect the filter to a centrifugal pump in this case.

A simple filter placed inside the tank, only separates debris and other substances and collects them at the bottom of the tank. These filters are still available in shops, but it is necessary to warn aquarists about their defects: in fact the accumulation of dirt and decomposing matter at the bottom of the tank is bound to pollute the water. This danger is partly obviated by the use of some filtering material enclosed within a container, placed inside the tank, as the area of infection is then reduced. A pipe comes out of the container (just a little above its base) through which air is sucked from below. The other end of the pipe is above the water level. The air circulation forces the dirty water through the filter layer which purifies it, and the cycle ends with the clean water passing through the return pipe back into the tank. To avoid the build-up of bacteria in the filter spreading to the water, it is necessary to remove it and clean it thoroughly once a week. This type of filter is, however, quite inadequate for marine aquaria. Should the inside filter be connected

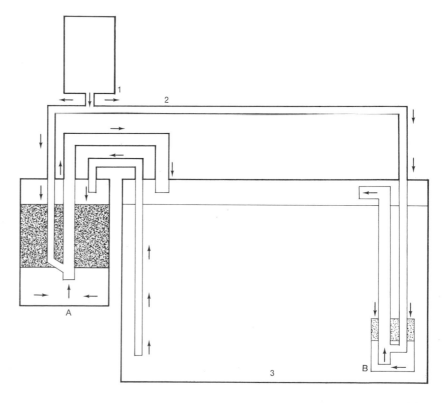

Diagram of: an external filter (A); and of an internal filter with chamber (B): 1, pump; 2, air pipe; 3, aquarium.

to a centrifuge pump, its efficiency would, in fact, be superior to that of an outside filter, as it allows for a quicker and more intense water purification.

A powerful filtering system is absolutely vital for a marine aquarium and therefore the use of a highly efficient set of filters is advisable. The best pump for this is the centrifugal type. The purpose of these installations should be that of producing a strong flow between the pump and the filtering system, as well as establishing a constant and strong process of purification. A large amount of dirt particles are then brought up and filtered, and the movement of the water has the added advantage of encouraging the fishes to swim all the time, and this strengthens their muscles, increases their resistance to disease, and activates their metabolism. Furthermore, many filtering systems enrich the water with extra air, thus providing more oxygen, which again is of benefit to the fishes' health. These results, however, cannot be achieved by an air pump but with a good water-and-air circulating system (centrifuge pump).

The strong current that such pumps generate causes a large deposit of dirt on the filter. It follows that the filtering agent must be changed much more often than is generally thought necessary – or even stated in the instructions. The absorption capacity of the filter is of short duration and the accumulation of dirt on it can, in some cases, pollute the water (waste materials collected on filters can soon breed bacteria). If, therefore, the filter is not cleaned often enough, it soon becomes a hotbed of infection. The same thing applies to a filter that is left inactive for several days or even hours. The water trapped in it soon becomes foul, and, when the filter is switched on again, this infected or dirty water will be pushed into the aquarium with results that range from the clouding of the water to the danger of infecting it with toxic substances. It is necessary, therefore, to make sure that the filtering material is perfectly clean every time the action of the filter has been interrupted, before switching the system on again. The most recent types of filters are easy to clean thoroughly, and are free of trouble and technical difficulties.

External filters operated by a centrifuge pump

Both filters and pumps are outside the water in this case, and are in a single unit. The entire volume of water in the tank is filtered within an hour. The filtering agent must be cleaned once a week (it can be changed and this, of course, entails a longer time). With the use of a nozzle on the return pipe, the water can be sprayed; thus extra aeration is supplied, but this is not to be taken as a substitute for the normal aeration required.

Internal filters operated by a centrifuge pump

The motor is outside the tank in this case, while the filter container is inside. The pump must be capable of emptying the tank within an hour at least. The filter unit is easily removed for a trouble-free cleansing operation. Cleaning should be carried out daily. There are other systems of centrifuge pump and filters coupled together available on the market, all more or less based on the same principle. Which filtering material should be used with a normal air filter? There are several possibilities and first we will discuss the purely mechanical filter.

Nylon wadding – even nylon stockings – can be used as a single filtering material. This catches the particles of dirt and can easily be washed. If cleaned daily, or several times a week, nylon wadding can last a long time. The more often this type of filter is cleaned, the longer the water remains fresh and free from impurities. Sand and pebbles can also be used in filters, but their use entails more work than that of nylon wadding.

The addition of some basalt stones to a mechanical filter will give it a chemical action too, as this igneous rock will release some trace elements into the water. Basalt gravel is not suitable to be used on its own, though, as it is not fine enough to give an efficient filtering action.

Activated charcoal has a combined double action as a chemical and mechanical filter. To avoid it getting dirty too quickly, a layer of nylon wadding can be put over it: this will intercept the dirt particles and should be changed daily, if possible. Activated charcoal has the ability to combine with most chemical substances – even drugs,

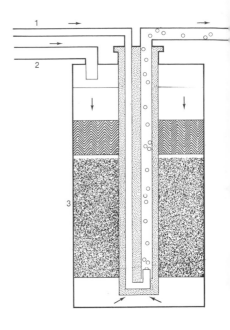

Diagram showing the purifying process of an external filter: 1, air flowing in; 2, water coming from the tank to be purified; 3, filtering agent; 4, purified water and air returning to the tank.

poisons, and dyes. However its purifying process is very slow, when it comes to bits of rubbish, dirt particles etc. Furthermore inorganic substances — including nitrates — are not eliminated by the activated charcoal (at least not in a noticeable quantity). Due to the fact that some trace elements can react and combine with substances that are released during the metabolic processes, which are then intercepted by the filter, a lack of trace elements can be caused by the indiscriminate use of activated charcoal. This is one of the reasons why activated charcoal is not used permanently in filters, but only periodically, as an alternative material; say for one or two days each week.

Anion-exchange type resins are also partially suitable filter materials. These very absorbent synthetic resins remove all substances produced by the protein during its decomposition process from amino acids to nitrate. Once again their permanent use would leave the water completely lacking in nitrates which — in the right amount — are necessary to the growth of algae. It seems that some synthetic resins are not tolerated by some particularly sensitive fishes. The constant use of synthetic resins also lowers the pH of the water and a continuous check should be kept on this. It should also be added that the resins cannot come into contact with the ozone and that — last, but not least — they deprive the water of its trace elements. Their permanent use, therefore, is not advisable.

Albumen purifier

The albumen purifier (or froth-scoop) aids the task of the filter in the aquarium. The principle of the system is based on the fact that when sea water containing a quantity of protein is shaken up it produces 'albumen froth', as is seen, for example, when a wave breaks along the shore. The majority of the scoops available in shops adopt the following system: the water from the tanks is piped — together with plenty of air — to a diffuser with a fine grille which is placed below a cylinder ('reaction chamber'); a bubbling action, similar to that of boiling liquid, is thus achieved. A whitish froth soon forms on the surface of the water with a top-layer floating constantly, which is the albumen foam. This foaming deposit is collected in the foam chamber placed on the upper part of the device: it is usually full of dirt and once settled, the liquid is usually greenish-brown and has an unpleasant smell. If possible, this container should be emptied daily or at least checked regularly. Needless to say that, once collected, the liquid should never be allowed to re-enter the aquarium, as its toxic property would prove fatal to the more delicate fishes. The more

Diagram of a filter unit to be placed outside the tank, using a centrifuge pump (Eheim system): 1, perforated pipe; 2, paddle wheel; 3, centrifuge pump; 4, suction pipe; 5, intake of water to be purified; 6, purifying agent. To the right: Diagram of a filter unit placed inside the tank, connected to a centrifuge pump: 1, motor; 2, paddle wheel; 3, filter; 4, air suction; 5, mixture of water and air.

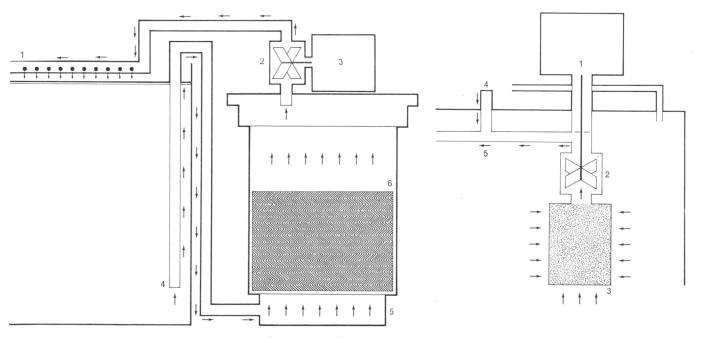

modern types of scoop are now connected to a centrifugal pump. If an ozonizer is coupled to the aerator, as already mentioned, the effect of the albumen purifier is at least doubled or can even become twenty times as efficient. This procedure is also followed when it is necessary to work with a greater quantity of ozone, without the risk of the fishes coming in direct contact with the gas. These devices, which are called ozonoreactors, are available commercially. The reaction chamber must be filled completely by bubbles of ozonized air blown upwards, otherwise the de-foaming action is either reduced or completely ineffective. The ozone gives a negative charge to the dirt particles, so that they combine with other particles. Thus they can easily be picked up by the air current and pushed upwards. This action stimulates the foaming and therefore the purification of the water. However, the amount of ozone introduced must be controlled, as an excess quantity can inhibit the foam from forming. The dose should be 4 to 7 mg of ozone per each 1000 litres of water.

Illumination

Many tropical fishes are true 'children of the sun'. Considering how brilliantly lit the coral reefs are, it is easy to understand why some aquarium inhabitants like a good light. Unfortunately some aquarists are rather ungenerous from this point of view. In some cases the fishes are so poorly supplied with light that they keep their night coloration throughout. There has been one occurrence of this even in a large public aquarium known to the writer.

Artificial light should never be cut off, even when the tank is near a window and some daily sunlight reaches it (although this must always be moderate), especially if some of the specimens are of tropical types. In fact, in the majority of cases, the sunlight does not last long enough and fishes do not enjoy enough daylight. Their colours, usually brilliant, do not show in full without strong light.

Fluorescent tubes are recommended as a source of illumination; they last longer and are more efficient, therefore they are less costly than the ordinary light bulb. Besides, with neon light it is possible to combine and integrate various components of the solar spectrum, so as to produce the required effect. An effective colour mixture is achieved with the light from one pink and two white tubes. If a cold light is desired the colour combination will be white and blue, instead. The aquarium can be lit either from the outside or from inside the tank. In the first instance the lights are placed on the cover, obviously not directly, but cushioned by some small supports made of cork, plastic, polyester or rubber. This method, though quite practical in itself, has a defect in that it wastes some of the shorter light waves, which will be absorbed by the glass of the lid, thus losing some of its effectiveness. Furthermore, the inside of the lid can easily mist up thus reducing the amount of light. The fluorescent tubes which can either float in water, or be fixed with a sucker at the bottom or on the sides of the tank, are more suitable. The heat generated by them helps to keep the water warm, too. However, the rubber seals present a slight drawback, as they deteriorate rather quickly in water, especially in the case of a marine aquarium. It is best, therefore, to choose tubes which have plastic seals. Algae tend to collect around the tubes floating on the water and these have to be cleaned at least once a week, but this is only a small snag.

The importance of ultra-violet rays should now be mentioned. The ordinary glass sides of an aquarium normally act as a filter and therefore these rays cannot get through to the water. As they aid plant growth and also have an antibiotic action, illumination by an ultra-violet ray lamp is particularly important for a marine aquarium. Either it can be placed directly in the tank or it can be coupled to the filter outside the tank, where it is directed towards the water which is going into the tank from the filter. The ultra-violet light can be left constantly switched on, thus obtaining a slightly antibiotic action; or it can be put on on particular occasions, when the water is not quite clean or there are some diseased fish. Once again this should only be regarded as an aid towards keeping the water clean and it is not enough on its own. It is sufficient, however, to clear muddy water.

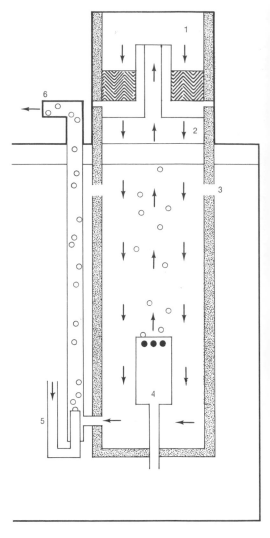

Diagram of an albumen-removing unit: 1, scoop; 2, reaction chamber; 3, inlet of water; 4, diffuser; 5, air blower; 6, pipe for the return of the water to the aquarium.

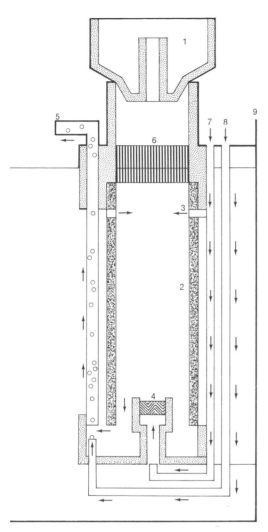

Diagram of an ozonizer unit (Sander system): 1, scooper; 2, reaction chamber; 3, inlet of water; 4, diffuser; 5, return water pipe; 6, grille for the filtering of foam; 7, duct for the mixture of air and ozone; 8, air duct; 9, aquarium frame.

Water heating and temperatures.

It is obviously important and usually generally necessary to heat the tank water for fishes that are of tropical origin, and for this the usual glass heater can be used. They should produce a water temperature ranging between 24° and 28°C. In the case of tropical fish a level below 20°C must be avoided. The capacity of the heater must be roughly matched to the volume of water in the tank; i.e. about 100 watts for each 100 litres of water. The position of the aquarium must also be taken into account as overheating can occur, especially if there is direct sun, while the heating may be insufficient if the surrounding atmosphere is cold. It is therefore advisable to install a heater with an electric thermostat, so that the water temperature is controlled by the switch outside the tank. The thermostat-controlled heater switches itself on and off automatically. Since the rubber parts of the heater tend to become porous through the action of the water (especially sea water), there is sometimes slight leakage which can upset the working of the thermostat. These parts should therefore be made of plastic. In any case it is wise to check the water temperature with a thermometer, twice daily, morning and evening.

The heating elements should be suspended in the water. To ensure an even temperature throughout the water, they should be located beside a diffuser or in the way of a current. They should not be suspended horizontally in the water or just left free on the bottom of the tank, as fishes could easily lie on them and run the risk of burning themselves.

With certain fish the thermometer should be protected. For example, fishes endowed with strong teeth, such as Porcupine fish, or Puffer fish or even Trigger fishes, can easily bite into it. It is therefore necessary to cover the thermometer and protect it thoroughly from fishes and also to use an alcohol thermometer rather than a mercury one, as mercury, if released in water, could easily prove to be lethal to fishes.

Fishes from northern seas, and also Mediterranean fishes, do not need heating in the water; indeed, they cannot tolerate an excessive increase in temperature: it should never be higher than 22°C for them. The water in the aquarium can overheat during the summer and this causes these fishes to suffer. A cooler place should be found for the aquarium or, if this is not possible, some other expedient adopted. Cold water from the tap can be run through the fresh water fish tank, for example; and for sea fishes a thin rubber tube can be put in the tank, with cold water passing through it before being discharged. With constant cold water circulating, the temperature drops sufficiently as a rule. A quicker and more drastic way is to put ice in the water. Some ice — either in a block or in small cubes from the refrigerator — can be put in a strong plastic bag and left to float on the surface of the water. Naturally the temperature must not be lowered more than necessary by this method otherwise the fishes will suffer. Some sea water can also be cooled down in the refrigerator and gradually poured into the tank. This operation may be necessary twice a day. The aquarist who has money and technical knowledge can buy and install a refrigeration unit (which is available in specialized shops) by which the water can be cooled to the right level of temperature.

Technical accessories

Aquarists should have a number of tools constantly at hand. They will be needed daily and are as important as the technical installation itself.

A thermometer is absolutely indispensable, irrespective of whether or not the tank is heated. With tropical fishes a constant check must be kept to ensure that the temperature of the water does not fall below the limit tolerated by the fishes, or does not overheat. On the other hand, Mediterranean fishes do not normally require heated water, and it can easily overheat in the summer and reach temperatures which are almost tropical, so that the aquarist must intervene. The efficiency of the thermometers is, however, somewhat doubtful, because the readings are not accurate (in the writer's personal experience): there can be a difference of up to 5 °C in the reading taken at the same time and condition with more than one thermometer of the same type. Temperature is a very important factor and its level must be controlled accurately, especially when sensitive tropical fishes are kept; it is therefore wise to make sure to buy a good accurate thermometer, rather than to save on the price.

There is a direct relationship between salinity and density, and it is necessary — when keeping a marine aquarium — to measure the density of the water and therefore at the same time its salt content. For this purpose an air meter or density meter must be used. The density value of the water is directly proportionate to the salinity: in fact, because of its salt content sea water has a higher specific weight than either fresh or distilled water. At a temperature of 4 °C one litre of pure water weighs 1 kg, while one litre of sea water has a weight ranging between 1·024 and 1·029 kg. This density value is the same as that of sea water. The more the sea water is diluted with fresh water, the less the salt content, the lower the weight and, therefore, the density.

Another important tool is a pair of tweezers which are used for several tasks, such as feeding the fishes, lifting objects out of the tank, etc. One or two pairs should be kept, one of the same length as the depth of the tank and one about 10 cm long, and they should be of non-rusting material, such as plastic or wood.

A real must for aquarists are a few small nets, in various shapes and sizes. The most versatile are the rectangular ones, as they can go easily into the corners of the tank. The larger ones can be used to catch the fast fishes. 'Catching bells' made of plastic or glass (and available in specialized shops) can also be used.

A scraper is necessary to remove moss and algae from the glass sides of the tank. A razor blade on a stick could be used, but there is the risk of scratching the glass. On the other hand, plastic scrapers are less efficient, even though safer.

To clean off the dirt which collects at the bottom, a siphon can be connected to the end of one of the pipes used to empty the tank (as, for instance, when the water must be partially changed).

Plastic pipes must be used for passing air from the pump to the aquarium, with T connections where branches in the pipes are necessary. Clips are used for controlling the air flow in the pipes. A floating food-distributor ring is used to give dry food to the fish. This prevents the food from spreading throughout the whole surface of the water. Worms can be put in a sieve, so that the fishes can pull them out one by one.

A thin spiral brush — such as those used for cleaning the inside of bottles — is advisable for removing dirt from filters, plastic pipes, etc. It is also wise to keep a couple of graded containers — one large (1 litre) and a smaller one — and two large white plastic buckets (also marked for measuring and with a lip, if possible). The owner of a marine aquarium also needs a 50- or a 100-litre container in which to prepare the artificial sea-water solution.

A length of 1 in-diameter pipe (either in rubber or plastic) must be kept for changing the water. All these small tools, so essential to an aquarist, are commonly sold in specialized shops.

Preparing the tank

There are many different ways of arranging the interior of an aquarium. The sides and the bottom may be left completely bare. For a completely 'hygienic aquarium' earthenware flowerpots with broken edges can be put on the bottom of the tank. These will serve as hide-outs or as artificial caves. If there are some cave-fish specimens among the aquarium inhabitants, plastic tubes can be put on the bottom for them. Nothing else is necessary, but if one wishes to have plants in the aquarium, they must be put in flowerpots filled with sand or gravel. This layout has an artificial look, but there are some advantages in it. The fishes can be watched easily, everything can be easily and quickly removed from the tank when it has to be cleaned, and lastly the fishes can be caught without difficulty. Although hygienic, this kind of aquarium seldom satisfies the aquarist's aesthetic sense. In contrast with it, there is the natural aquarium. This is made up from the various elements of a particular natural environment — in our case, the habitat of aquatic animals, i.e. the different types of natural background of the various species of fish, either freshwater or marine. In lakes, marshes and rivers the ground is usually thickly covered with vegetation, while along the seashore there are rocks, sandy beaches or coral reefs. The object is to reproduce one of these environments in the aquarium. In order to achieve the desired effect various decorative materials are used (such as wood, stones, corals, etc.) as well as sand and plants. Naturally the decorative layout must be completed before the tank is filled with water.

Preparation of the freshwater aquarium

The bottom of the tank is first covered with a mixture of gravel and sand. The organic waste of the fishes is sufficient for fertilizing the plants in the tank. White sand and quartz gravel are obtained in shops, but are not tolerated by a number of fishes and plants due to their brightness. The best answer, therefore, is to obtain sand from a river, provided that it is unpolluted.

The sand used for the bottom layer must be thoroughly washed beforehand. To do this, half-fill a bucket with the sand to be washed and pass a pipe through it right down to the bottom; connect the other end of the pipe to a tap. The water pressure will agitate the sand and cause dirt particles — which are lighter — to come to the surface and be carried away by the water overflowing the bucket. It should take about ten minutes to obtain sufficiently clean sand. Transfer the clean sand into the empty tank and either level it out flat or make it into a slope (8 to 10 cm high at the back, 3 to 4 cm at the front). A terraced arrangement can be achieved, if desired, with the use of some stones. At any rate the whole bottom layer must be completed before water is poured into the aquarium. It is possible that at first, in spite of the fact that the sand has been washed, the water will appear cloudy, but it clears again after a few days.

It could be quite enough to have a good arrangement of plants and nothing else in the aquarium. Obviously, however, other elements can be introduced, provided that they are natural and fit in with the particular environment chosen. In a freshwater aquarium there are two types of material which can be used: stone and wood. Stones make an attractive and natural decoration. They can be arranged singly or in piles; a little cave can be built with them, or they can be scattered all over the bottom. Often stones by providing hiding places for fishes give them a natural sense of being protected, so that to the aesthetic function of the stones is also added a biological role.

Caution must be used when selecting stones for the aquarium, as some of them can release substances which dissolve in water and have a toxic effect on some fishes. Limestone — or any stone containing lime salt — must never be used in aquariums, because this is soluble in water and makes it 'hard'. Stones which contain metal are also to be excluded (as, for example, red sand stone that contains iron); particularly attractive coloured stones contain heavy metals which are rather poisonous.

Before being placed in the tank, the stones must be thoroughly washed (under running water and without detergents) and well scrubbed.

Care must be taken that they are placed in a safe position, so that they cannot roll against the glass sides of the tank. It must be remembered also that fishes love rummaging around the sand and that they can easily overturn a stone if it is set vertically, and not resting firmly, on the bottom.

Wood can create an impressive appearance in a freshwater aquarium, be it in the form of a knotty branch or a small log. Wood can also be combined with stones or with plants and in large aquaria a complete landscape can thus be satisfactorily achieved.

Many kinds of wood tend to go soft and rot, thus polluting the water. It is best, therefore, to choose woods which have already been equipped to survive by natural forces: these are the partly fossilized woods which have been submerged in water for centuries and only brought to the surface when marshland is reclaimed. This 'marsh wood' can be obtained from specialized shops.

Before being placed in an aquarium it must be thoroughly scrubbed and washed under running water and then boiled for two hours. While the wood is boiling, it absorbs enough water to prevent it floating and it will therefore rest firmly on the bottom of the tank. Coconut shells cut in half can also be put at the bottom and, if an opening is cut at one side, they make attractive caves. These, too, must be previously cleaned and boiled in the same way as the marsh wood.

In a marine aquarium an interesting and natural environment can be reproduced by building rocky 'shores', coral reefs, and sandy patches. In this case it is safe to use limestone. Some different habitats can be combined, with alternate patches of rock and corals and sandy surfaces, and in this way different types of fishes can be put together and feel at home.

A layer of sand is absolutely necessary for the species that live on, or under, the sand. To these can be added those fishes that love plenty of space in which to swim freely; particularly suitable to this type of aquarium are Grey Mullet and many species of Wrasse. A distinction must be made between the species that live on the bottom sand – or in the sand – and the free swimmer. The sand dwellers need a fairly deep layer (10 to 20cm); this is particularly true in the case of Wrasses that completely bury themselves in sand at any hint of danger and for sleeping at night. The Jawfishes build holes in sand topped just like chimney pots. Among species of invertebrates, some sea anemones live in sandy zones and their 'foot' is solidly anchored to the bottom while the body must be covered by at least 10cm of sand. Many molluscs also live at the bottom of the aquarium.

When the layer of sand is extended right to the front of the aquarium, it impedes the view and spoils the whole effect. It is best, therefore, to build the sand into terraces with, say, two or even three steps, the lowest at the front. The terraces can be bounded by stones long enough to form a kind of small wall. To join the stones one can either use adhesive, or put sea shells in front of the wall, forming an artificial barrier which will stop the sand escaping between the stones. The sides and the back walls of a tank with a sandy bottom layer can be adorned in various ways. For instance, some blue paper can be put on the outside of the back wall of the tank, giving an effect of great depth. Since, however, sand is very often next to a rocky bank some high, flat stones or branches of coral could be put against the back wall. In this way the surroundings would also be more suitable to those fishes that enjoy rough and ragged contours. There are also some reproductions of coral or rock seascapes which can be put at the back of the tank, giving an illusion of real rocky shores, or coral reefs.

If a sandy layer is put on the bottom of the aquarium, it must be remembered that when it reaches a certain depth it can become a real hotbed for infection. When the sand has very fine grains, it tends to pack solid and become less and less porous. Partly through lack of air and partly because of food residues and other organic impurities the decomposition process sets in and gradually the sand becomes a putrefying mass of mud. If this is shaken, the water becomes cloudy and infected. Often some bluish patches appear on the light-coloured sand, especially in the deeper layers (this happens both in freshwater and marine aquaria). This polluted sand represents a great danger to all the inhabitants of the tank, because it is toxic. There is a good alarm system to warn us of this danger: when the fins of the Wrasses (these fishes hide in the sand at night to sleep) become ragged and torn to the point when the fishes cannot swim properly, there is no doubt that the sand has deteriorated and is in the process of becoming polluted.

To prevent this happening, it is necessary to sift through the sand systematically – removing the infected parts – and change it, either in part or completely. Another method is to put a fine nylon sieve between the layer of sand and the bottom of the aquarium. Instead of putting the inlet pipe on the upper part, in this case, the clean water from the pump will be directed underneath the sand in the tank: in this way the sand is moved all the time by the jet of water underneath, and dirt residues will not collect at the bottom of the tank. The simplest solution, however, is to remove the sand from the tank at least once a week and wash it thoroughly — with the help of a pump — so that all dirt is removed. The type of sand used is of some importance, too: generally quartz sand of a fairly coarse grain (1 to 1·5mm in diameter) is advisable, as this keeps clean better than any other. Fine sand collected from the sea is not advisable, because it can easily become too closely packed. A mixture of the following ingredients is very good: crushed coral fragments and finely chopped sea shells (the empty valves of mussels which are kept as food for the fishes, for instance), in the proportions of one to one, mixed with quartz sand or the aquarium sand commonly sold in shops. The sand will remain aerated because of the coral fragments — which are rather coarse — and the sea shells. Furthermore, invertebrates take some of the substance necessary for their growth and skeleton development from the fragments of shell and coral.

The rocky aquarium should be as varied in its appearance as is a natural rocky coastline. The rocks are normally ragged with cracks and breaks and they often overhang and form caves. These conditions can be easily reproduced given a little knowhow. The whole of the back wall of the tank should be covered in rocks. Magmatic rocks (such as quartz, basalt, granite, porphyry etc.) and occasionally also calcareous rocks (for example, dolomite) can be used, provided they are not reddish, as these contain metal. The stones can be piled up on one another to form a wall, or they can be stuck with a special adhesive, which is commonly available. To this rocky layout can be added a terraced effect: a shorter piece can be placed in front of an overhanging rock (in the field of composition one can give one's imagination free rein, so long as exaggeration and overdecoration are avoided). It is not advisable to be restricted by the use of rocks alone: the best way is to leave a space at the front where sand or gravel can be placed. Gobies, Blennies and Scorpion-fishes live among rocks, as do Wrasses, Sea Perches, and other families of Perciformes, Morays, etc. Many invertebrates also inhabit rocky shores: sea anemones, starfishes, sea urchins, crabs, etc. Rocks are normally covered in algae, too. If the back is covered by rocks and the front part left free — with a sandy patch at the bottom — there will be ample room for the fishes to swim about: this arrangement will therefore leave a wider choice regarding the fishes that can be kept in an aquarium.

A most interesting decoration from a biological point of view is provided by 'living rocks' — i.e. pieces of rock, stones or large shells taken directly from the sea (for example, the Mediterranean shores) entirely covered with moss, seaweed, small animals and sponges, and other living organisms. These rocks brighten up the aquarium and can also contribute towards keeping it healthy.

The coral-reef aquarium needs some preparation before its layout can be designed. The aquarist should have some practical knowledge about aquaria and rocks, before attempting to make this type of aquarium. The basic arrangement, to which may be added an infinite number of variations, is the same as that suggested above for the rock aquarium. At the back of the tank some pieces of coral skeletons may be arranged in a reef formation, while the front is left free, with just a sandy layer at the bottom. In their natural environment the branches of corals are firmly anchored to calcareous rocks on the sea-bed, but after they have been torn off to be sold in shops, they are no longer very stable. Often some fishes love raking through the sand at the bottom of the tank, and this can cause the whole arrangement of corals, so lovingly put together, to become unstable and even to tumble down. It is best, therefore, to fix each individual coral branch to a stone (pumice is very suitable for this) which must be hidden, by a layer of coral pieces stuck to it with adhesive. A base of clay the same length as the tank can be made in the form of a long roll, and the coral branches fixed to it. The branches are then removed and the holes slightly enlarged before putting the clay base into a kiln for setting.

Colours, as well as shapes, are important in a coral reef. The dark red Organ-pipe coral is the most commonly found in shops, but there are also some ranging from white to shades of yellow, purple or creamy pink. This display of colours, however, bears no resemblance to a natural coral reef. In reality, a coral reef is covered by masses of polyps which are greenish or brown. When the polyps are dead a white calcareous skeleton can be seen. The Organ-pipe coral is the only coral with a red skeleton. When a whole branch of corals dies on a coral reef it is quickly covered by algae, moss, and other living organisms that cling to it firmly. The same happens in an aquarium, so that the artificial-looking white or red of the skeletons soon disappears, and a rock covered by algae offers a much more natural sight in an aquarium than those which are brightly coloured.

Obviously there should not be any Mediterranean fishes in a coral-reef aquarium but only tropical species indigenous to coral reefs. A list of 'coral-reef fishes' is too long to be given here.

It must be pointed out that, however pleasing to the eye, an artificial coral reef has its inconveniences. A dead fish may become trapped in the branches and, if this is not discovered immediately, it can cause infection in the water. The same applies to remnants of food caught up in the branches where they rot, as well as to any impurity stirred up in the water by the fishes. There is no risk of fishes cutting themselves on the points of the corals, as they are naturally used to living amongst coral reefs. When a fish has to be caught, however, corals present a great obstacle. The net gets tangled up in them and is often torn, while the fish can easily find inaccessible hiding places among them. Very often it follows that the whole structure must be taken down. This means a great deal of trouble for the aquarist who has often been tempted into sticking the branches together. The work of dismantling it is, however, far less complicated if the coral branches have been stuck singly on a stone or inserted one by one in the holes of the clay base.

Blocks or pieces of coral bought in shops generally look very clean. However, they should still be inspected carefully before being placed in the aquarium. It must be remembered that this calcareous and porous stone is of animal origin and that not only was it covered by living cells, but had living cells within it, too. In spite of the clean appearance, remnants of these living organisms can still be hidden in the tiny pores and, as soon as they come into contact with water, they begin to rot. A piece of coral, therefore, that has not been thoroughly cleaned, can turn the water into a foul-smelling liquid in no time at all.

The only way to clean coral skeletons is to boil them for a few hours, and then leave them to soak in a container made of either wood, plastic or earthenware, for about 5 to 6 hours in a very salty water-solution. Then, if when it is taken out and rinsed, the coral has no unpleasant odour, it can be safely placed in the aquarium. Should it smell, however, it must be placed in caustic soda for 10 to 13 days and subsequently under running water for a further two weeks. To avoid the tiresome process of boiling the same result can be achieved by soaking the coral in a 15% caustic-soda solution for 6 to 10 days, and rinsing it under running water for 10 to 14 days. With both these methods, great care should be taken when handling the caustic-soda solution, which can be very dangerous if not used with care, especially with children about. If particularly brilliant and clean-looking coral are desired, they can be put in a peroxide-water bath (10% solution for a period of 8 days), dried out in the open air, and finally rinsed under running water for another 8 days. The only thing to remember is that this whiteness will not last for long. It is never advisable to use hydrochloric acid on corals in order to clean them, because the limestone dissolves and, after the treatment, little would be left of the most fantastic coral branch.

On the whole, two things must be remembered when planning for a natural aquarium: first of all, that the various elements must not be put together indiscriminately, but according to a prearranged plan; and secondly that a natural landscape is never completely sym-metrical. When the background of the aquarium is made up of rocks or coral reef, and in the foreground there is an unbroken stretch of sand, the view presented tends to be rather monotonous. A large shell or a sprig of coral stuck in the sand will make a pleasant addition. The aquarist who wants to make his aquarium attractive must use his imagination. Some knowledge of interior decoration and landscaping could be useful when arranging the objects in an aquarium.

It is advisable for beginners not to overdo the amount of decoration, at least to start with. The first attempts should be limited to putting a little sand at the bottom, and placing some decorative objects (stones, shells) in a simple design without using corals. Only gradually, with practice, can the final decoration be completed.

Experience is needed when building up the back wall. To give more depth, some aquarists prefer the addition of rocks put outside the aquarium at the back: the trouble is that, with time, the rocks inside get more and more covered with algae, while the ones on the outside of the tank gather more and more dust with an incongruous result, in which the sense of depth gets lost. Some stick-on colour prints reproducing more or less faithfully views of rocky banks or even coral reefs, are now available on the market.

Some specialized shops also sell many decorative objects for aquaria that have little or nothing at all to do with the fishes' natural environment: submerged castles, figures of underwater fishermen, dwarfs (more suitable perhaps for miniature gardens), mermaids etc. that are in extremely bad taste. These objects, from a biological point of view, are meaningless and, apart from anything else, they have no aesthetic justification: however, they can be included as embellishments of the aquarium if desired. Two things must be remembered, though. Fishes can cut or injure themselves on any sharp corners on these objects. Some of the colours used to paint them (or even the materials used for their manufacture) can often release toxic substances which are dangerous to the animals. It would definitely be in bad taste to include such objects in a marine aquarium which contains coral reefs, as corals themselves already have such fantastic shapes and are far superior in beauty to any other object.

Safety Measures

Electric current near water – and especially sea water – is a great source of danger, as the salt deposits, inevitably settling on lighting points, can cause electrical shocks. The damp around a tank tends to cause corrosion of the metal parts of switches kept near it, and they therefore should be used with caution. The electric heater rods can burst and transmit the current to the water. Neglecting safety precautions can endanger not only the fish, but also human lives. It must also be added that very often electrical appliances sold for aquarium use are not up to safety standards, and some are definitely dangerous. This, of course, is particularly so with the cheaper ranges. The fact that water – especially if salty – is an excellent conductor should never be forgotten when working near an aquarium, and even a 60-volt shock could prove lethal.

It is therefore vital that the following precautions are observed:

1. All electrical appliances must be earthed.

2. The floor, the tank, the lid and all electrical appliances must be kept scrupulously dry (especially things such as lamps and filter pumps). Salt encrustations should be washed off with fresh water; lids and lamps need to be washed at least once a week.

3. Whenever work is being carried out on electrical installations, the plug should be removed from the socket: switching off whatever appliance is being worked on is not enough. Make sure the hands are perfectly dry when touching switches and plugs. The filter-pump switches are particularly dangerous in this respect: the salt contained in a few drops of sea water is enough to transfer the electricity supply to the outside surface.

4. Remove the bulb on the aquarium lid, before opening the aquarium. The glass sides do not offer much grip when lifting the lid, and it could easily slip and fall into the water. If this happens and the bulb touches the water, the least that could be expected is a short circuit, but there is a real danger of something happening which goes beyond the mere breaking of the bulb or even the death of the fishes. Under no circumstances be tempted to put your hand into the water in order to get the bulb out: first disconnect the plug – with dry hands – and only then proceed to fish out the lamp.

5. The heaters must never be touched unless the plug is disconnected. This precaution must always be taken before starting any kind of work and, in particular before changing the water in the tank. Heater elements, when connected, should never have more than 3 cm of their length sticking out above the surface, or they can burst as soon as they get hot. This can also happen when the heating is turned on again by the thermostatic control after hours or days. A heater can burst if the solder of the seal has broken loose (generally due to bacterial corrosion). To guard against this, the heaters should be checked to make sure that all rubber parts are smooth: if they become sticky to the touch, they must be replaced. All heaters must be specially designed for immersion in water.

6. Heaters and thermostat elements must not be completely immersed in water when they have a control device at the top. The rubber cap must be always kept dry.

7. Big fishes like to swim near the heater and, if this is not securely fixed, they can easily push it against the walls of the tank. To avoid possible damage it is best to hang the heaters in a corner, or fix them at the bottom of the aquarium; in fact a broken heater would involve the danger that we have already pointed out to aquarists.

8. Small repairs (changing a plug, etc.) can be carried out by the aquarist, but anything more complicated is best left to an electrician. It is advisable to have a voltameter that is sensitive enough to detect small leaks so that all possible risks can be prevented. This is particularly important in marine aquaria.

Feeding

Good health and normal behaviour in fishes also depend on their diet. Many species survive on *Tubifex* as dry food, but this is monotonous. The skilful aquarist is able to provide a varied diet for his animals.

Many fishes spend the whole day in search of food. This is particularly true of the species that feed on underwater flora, small organisms (found on the sea-bed) and plants, or those that love rummaging in the mud or live on plankton. They eat very little at a time, but do it all day long. Predators, on the other hand, generally rest for a day or two, after each large meal.

The species that eat little and often should be fed frequently: if possible every hour. It is not wise to feed them only once a day particularly where some delicate coral-fish species are concerned. For a number of freshwater fishes, sieves full of Tubifex, floating distributor rings, or automatic feeders are more than sufficient for the right dosage and regular distribution of food. These feeding techniques, on the other hand, cannot be used for the majority of marine fishes.

Beginners often — mistakenly — tend to give too much food. It is useful to remember that temperatures are rather high in aquaria and uneaten food can very quickly go bad. It is best, therefore to give the animals as much food as they can eat in five minutes, after which, the food should be removed from the tank.

A varied diet is very important. With some species of fish it is not only necessary to feed them several times a day but also to give different food as well. Fishes are often changeable as to their likes and dislikes: they will eat something one week which they refuse the next, and then eat again the week after. A varied diet is therefore an important condition for their welfare. Furthermore, only take enough for one meal at a time from your frozen food supply.

Food for Freshwater fishes

1. Artificial food. The most important is the dry variety that is sold in flakes, which contains a balanced mixture of substances, prepared according to sound diet principles; it should contain fats, carbohydrates and trace elements, as well as albumen. Food especially prepared for particular species (such as Guppies, Carps, etc.) is available in shops. Many fishes take artificial food quite willingly, either as a paste or in cake form. Naturally, the food cakes are only suitable for species that

have strong teeth, while the paste is particularly apt for young fishes.

2. To give as wide a variety as possible, some small animals (either alive or only just dead) should be supplied. Many freshwater fishes live happily on *Tubifex*, water fleas, mosquito larvae — red or white — and, occasionally, on copepods. These small animals can be caught in ponds, marshes, and wells with gauze nets, or can be bought in special shops. *Tubifex* generally live in mud, while most of the others swim freely in water.

The larvae of Brine Shrimps are important live food for many fry of marine and freshwater species. The aquarist must keep the eggs in salt water, and follow the instructions generally issued with the purchase of the eggs. A special breeding container can also be bought, but a plastic bucket could be used in its place. It must be pointed out that, on their own, neither Brine Shrimp larvae nor water fleas should be given as a complete diet.

Some less valuable Guppies should be bred as food for predators — i.e. those fishes that live on smaller fishes. This entails the provision of a suitable container for breeding. As soon as they are born fry should be separated from the mother and other adult fishes, which are likely to devour them. As a substitute for their normal diet some fishes will eat calves' liver cut into thin strips, raw fish, or meat (this, though, could transmit diseases). A lettuce leaf should be given daily to herbivorous fishes (obviously only as a supplement to their main diet which consists of algae and dry food). The lettuce should be thoroughly washed before being put in the aquarium, as it may have been treated with insecticides which are extremely poisonous to fish. The remains of the leaf must be removed from the tank water before it begins to rot.

Food for marine fishes

Many sea fishes — in particular those that feed on plankton and the herbivorous species, for example Damsel fishes and Blennies — seem to like dry food. Fishes with strong teeth, such as Trigger fishes, like food cakes.

Mysis, Brine Shrimps, amphipods, and small crabs make a good live food and they swim freely in water. The species that have strong teeth (Wrasses, Trigger fishes) like to crunch small bivalves, or even crabs — some of these are available as fish food (fresh or frozen). Fillet of mussels, cut into strips of varying size to suit different-sized fishes, is an important component in the diet of many species. In many cases filleted fresh fish (untreated) can also be used, as well as fresh roes.

Tubifex, *Enchytrea*, mosquito larvae, cyclops, amphipods and lastly gastropods and freshwater fishes can be given as a substitute. These animals when used as food must be consumed quickly, otherwise the meat deteriorates, affecting the quality of the tank water.

In the absence of something better, some carnivorous fishes eat calves' liver or hearts (cut into thin strips or minced, according to the fishes' preference).

Lettuce is given as a vegetable diet (provided it is well washed). Sea lettuce or algae can be collected by those aquarists who live near the sea.

Living rocks

The so-called 'living rocks' have been found to be exceptionally useful for the efficient running of marine aquaria. They are stones or pieces of rock — taken from the seashore — that are covered in various species of algae, as well as bryozoa, sponges, coelenterates and other sessile invertebrates. These stones are useful for the growth of algae in the aquarium and stimulate the production of the plankton, while they can be eaten by some fishes as their natural food. For tropical fishes, for instance coral-reef fishes, rocks taken from the Mediterranean are generally suitable.

It must be pointed out that many animal organisms and plants living on these rocks are particularly sensitive to drugs — especially those containing copper — and antibiotics. When drugs are given to fishes it is necessary to remove the stones and keep them separate for the time required.

Quarantine

Newly acquired fishes should never be placed in an established aquarium straight away, but kept in quarantine in a separate tank. They should remain there under observation for at least three weeks, especially if they are marine species. The tank should be very simply equipped: for instance, it should have caves that are easy to inspect (made of pieces of rock and broken earthenware vessels) and be equipped with aeration, filtering and heating systems. A 30-litre tank in glass or plastic can be used.

Recently imported tropical fishes should remain in this tank for two weeks at a temperature of 28° to 30°C. The fishes must be watched very closely, paying attention to the condition of their skin, fins, etc. In this relatively high temperature – which obviously requires plenty of aeration – any disease which may be incubating will soon develop. If no symptoms appear, the temperature can be lowered to 24° to 26°C. Generally these precautions are sufficient to complete a quarantine. In fact, if the fishes do not have either skin parasites, or disease of any kind, they can be put directly into an established aquarium. However, if preferred, they can be first given a preventive medical treatment, for which specific drugs can be bought.

The new arrivals, especially marine fishes, can also be given a bath in water containing an antibiotic which will help dry up the mucus on their skin, thus removing the parasites more quickly. The dosage is 200,000 international units of soluble penicillin for each litre of water, either fresh or sea water (therefore, for a 30-litre tank 6,000,000 units will be used). The fishes must not be left in this water for longer than twelve hours or there is a risk of poisoning. A vigorous aeration is recommended during this bath. Filtering must be stopped. Throughout the period of treatment the fishes must be under close observation. Another important method of treatment is a copper-based bath (see section on 'Diseases'). Once again, the water temperature should be slightly increased, and strong aeration is required. Filtering should be in action, but only a mechanical filter should be used: one of the best is nylon-wadding. After 2 to 3 weeks of this treatment the temperature is lowered to 24° to 28°C and the fishes can be transferred to the aquarium after a few days. During the quarantine period the fishes should be given a normal diet. It must be remembered, though, that a quarantine involving a treatment based on any drugs, as this is not a natural state, can have dangers. A fish, weak from its capture and the journey, may not be able to tolerate the quarantine treatment (and may even die) while it might have had a good chance of recovering and surviving had it been put in a healthy established aquarium on arrival.

Diseases

The loving care we lavish on our fishes can entail sadness as well as joy. Indeed both freshwater and sea-dwellers easily succumb to illness. Several successful experiments have been recorded with regard to diseases of freshwater fishes. By contrast, very little is yet known about diseases of sea fishes. The old principle that diseases can only be prevented in the best living conditions is still valid. In this ideal case, a germ has little chance of surviving against the natural defence-mechanism of a fish. However, even minor faults, such as an overcrowded aquarium, the imperfect condition of the water, some wrong food, etc., can alter the ideal balance, thus causing illness. Unfortunately, as a rule it will not be just one fish, but the whole of the aquarium which is infected.

The question is, how can symptoms be recognized. Fins flat against the body; swimming movements disconnected and jerky; a tendency to scratch the body against stones and corals; quick breathing; remaining on the surface of the water; refusal of food; excessive mucus produced on the skin; swimming in a rolling action; remaining inactive at the bottom (when fishes are normally good swimmers) — all these are significant signs that an infection is present. The aquarist must take precautions as soon as he sees any of these symptoms (they are only very slight at the onset of an illness).

One must fear the worst and give a prescription of a general nature. The ignorance of specialized suppliers is often appalling. It is not a rare occasion when diseased fishes are sold either in ignorance or greed. It is therefore advisable to examine the fishes very closely when purchasing them. Most diseases in fishes are of a parasitic nature. Whenever water deteriorates — often even after being changed — some coral-reef fishes can suddenly become covered by a mass of parasites. It looks, in fact, as though they are smothered in flour or semolina. By taking immediate action and giving the appropriate drugs, it is possible to save the rest of the animals in the aquarium. On the other hand, torn and ragged fins, little bumps, swellings, sores, swollen bellies, dull eyes, unusual growths or loss of weight, are symptoms of much more serious infections. Naturally some of these symptoms, for instance a torn fin, can often be traced back to a little accident, due, for instance, to a fight between animals. Besides, most of the imported fishes are bound to feel weak on arrival and their defences against disease are lowered; this is particularly true of tropical fishes. It is impossible to give full details of all the various diseases in this chapter. We shall only mention the most important. Freshwater fishes are often affected by *Ichthyophthirius* (White Spot), a parasite carrier that gives white dots all over the skin. If it is not cured at once, the fish dies. There are various commercial preparations sold for this: any one can be used provided that the instructions are followed. It is best to remove the fish to a quarantine tank, as the drugs could affect plant life in the aquarium. All fishes should be removed, as it is almost certain that they, too, have been affected by the same parasite. It is not necessary to change the water in the aquarium because the parasites do not live more than a few days in the absence of fishes.

A disease that often attacks marine fishes is *Oodinium ocellatum*. The stricken fishes become covered by a white encrustation (sometimes it can also be darker), rather like an outbreak of *Ichthyophthirius* in freshwater species. In the beginning there are a few white points that look like grains of semolina on the body. Fishes tend, at this stage, to rub against sand or corals. In the next stage, the whole body is covered completely as though with flour. When the growth extends over the gills, respiration becomes difficult, and death by soffocation follows. The carrier organism is a flagellate parasite that generallly is harboured on the skin and in the gills of a fish. If the illness is cured in time, the fish can recover.

There are many cures for this disease. The safest and most efficient is the copper treatment (this is a prolonged immersion in a bath of copper sulphate that can be bought in specialized shops. The proportion used is 0·163 g of copper sulphate for each 100 litres of sea water). An equal proportion of sulphate is added every two or three days, as it gradually tends to separate. The treatment must continue until the white growth disappears and the fish returns to its normal behaviour. A partial change of water must be given at the end of the treatment. Invertebrates (crabs, molluscs, sea anemones etc.) and plants cannot tolerate the treatment and die, and therefore they should be removed beforehand. *Oodinium* will survive in a tank without fishes, unlike *Ichthyophthirius*.

There can be outbreaks of exophthalmia (infection of the outer eye). It is caused by tuberculosis of fishes or other carriers that harbours in the front part of the eye; haematoma, or monotonous food. The most common cause is, however, stale water. First of all change the water. At times a pH variation or a drop of density can also work wonders. A course of antibiotic drugs is effective, too.

Capture and transport of aquarium specimens

Any aquarist derives pride and joy in the personal capture of his specimens, carried out in a natural environment (Mediterranean, Red Sea, North Africa, Indian Ocean, or even inland waters). Both capture and transport, however, require technical skill and knowledge.

The equipment used for the capture of fishes must be so designed as not to cause damage. Fishes captured with line and hook are not generally brought into aquaria, because of the wounds they inevitably suffer.

The capture is more or less a game of patience, but the transport and care of the live fishes between the time they are caught and their introduction to an aquarium presents complications and problems. Very seldom is there an aquarium near at hand along the shore where they are captured into which they could be placed for immediate survival. The fishing-boat tanks that are also used by our lake and river fishermen will be useful to keep the fishes until they are ready to be transported. They will be anchored in the river, lake or along the seashore. Equally useful for this purpose are plastic buckets with some holes at the sides and a lid; or similar containers.

Packing the fish and the journey itself present much greater difficulties. The use of plastic bags (use at least two, one inside the other) two thirds full of water and one third oxygen has proved to be quite satisfactory. An oxygen bottle should therefore be kept at hand. Recently, some oxygenating tablets have been on sale (the dosage is given on the packet) and these provide a simple way of giving the water the necessary oxygen. Fishes and many invertebrates seem to do well with this method and do not need aeration. If possible place only one fish in each packet. Precautions must be taken to avoid the fishes getting overheated during the journey (this is quite a possibility going through hot countries, such as Arabia, Africa, and even Europe, when the fishes are in a car parked in direct sunlight). They must be protected against low temperatures that can occur (for instance, on an air journey or when travelling across a mountain). It is always advisable to place the plastic bags or glass bowls, etc., containing the fishes, in boxes insulated with polystyrene or similar material. During transportation the fishes do not require food.

Having completed his journey and brought the fishes back, the successful aquarist can now look forward to doing all the work described in the previous sections of this book.

Bibliography

Aquaria in General

AXELROD H. R. and VORDERWINKLER W., *Saltwater Aquarium Fish.* TFH Publ., Jersey City, 1965.

INNES W. T., *Exotic Aquarium Fishes.* Innes Publ. Comp., Philadelphia, 1954.

LODEWIJKS J. M., *Tropical Fish in the Aquarium.* Blandford, London.

MADSEN J. M., *Aquarium Fishes in Colour.* Blandford, London, 1975.

WALKER B., *Tropical Fish in Colour.* Blandford, London.

WELLS A. L., *Tropical Aquariums, Plants and Fishes.* Warne, London, 1954.

Plants

DE WIT H. C. D., *Aquarium Plants.* Blandford Press, London, 1964.

FASSETT N. C., *Manual of Aquatic Plants.* MacGraw Hill, New York and London, 1940.

Fish

AXELROD H. R., *Freshwater Fishes.* TFH Publ., Jersey City, 1974.

BURGESS W. and AXELROD H.R., *Pacific Marine Fishes.* Books 1–5. TFH Publ., Jersey City, 1973–74.

BURTON M., *Encyclopedia of Fish.* Octopus, London, 1975.

CIHAR J., *A Colour Guide to Freshwater Fishes.* Octopus, London, 1975.

DUTTA R., *Tropical Fish.* Octopus, London, 1975.

FRANK S., *The Pictorial Encyclopaedia of Fishes.* Hamlyn, London, 1971.

GOLDSTEIN R. J., *Cichlids.* TFH Publ., Jersey City, 1970.

GOLDSTEIN R. J., *Anabantoids.* TFH Publ., Jersey City, 1971.

HERALD E. S., *Living Fishes of the World.* Hamish Hamilton, London, 1961.

HOEDEMAN J. J., *Naturalists' Guide to Freshwater Aquarium Fish.* Sterling Publishing Co., New York, 1974.

JACOBS K., *Livebearing Aquarium Fishes.* Studio Vista, London, 1971.

JULIAN T. W., *The Concise Encyclopedia of Tropical Fish.* Octopus, London, 1974.

MARSHALL N. B., *The Life of Fishes.* Weidenfeld & Nicolson, London, 1965.

MUUS B. J. and DAHLSTROM P., *The Freshwater Fishes of Britain and Europe.* Collins, London, 1971.

MUUS B. J. and DAHLSTROM P., *The Sea Fishes of Britain and North-Western Europe.* Collins, London, 1974.

SCHUL J., *Rivulins of the Old World.* TFH Publ., Jersey City, 1968.

SCHINDLER O., *Freshwater Fishes.* Thames & Hudson, London, 1957.

STERBA G., *Freshwater Fishes of the World.* Vista Books, London, 1962.

WHEELER A., *Fishes of the World — an Illustrated Dictionary.* Macmillan Pub. Co. Inc., New York, 1975.

WHEELER A., *Fishes of the British Isles and North West Europe.* Macmillan & Co. Ltd., London, 1969.

Invertebrates

ANGEL H. and ANGEL M., *Ocean Life.* Octopus, London, 1975.

BARRETT J. and YONGE C. M., *Pocket Guide to the Seashore.* Collins, London, 1958.

BUCHSBAUM R. and MILNE L. J., *Living Invertebrates of the World.* Hamish Hamilton, London, 1960.

INGLE R. W., *A Guide to the Seashore.* Hamlyn, London, 1969.

MACAN T. T., *A Guide to Freshwater Invertebrate Animals.* Longmans, London, 1960.

MELLANBY H., *Animal Life in Freshwater.* Methuen, London, 1963.

YONGE C. M., *The Sea Shore.* Collins, London, 1966.

Index

Page numbers in *italics* refer to illustrations.